American Book Company's

PASSING THE
GEORGIA 7TH GRADE CRCT
IN SCIENCE

Written to GPS 2006 Standards

Michelle Gunter

American Book Company
PO Box 2638
Woodstock, GA 30188-1383
Toll Free: 1 (888) 264-5877   Phone: (770) 928-2834
Fax: (770) 928-7483 Toll Free Fax: 1 (866) 827-3240
Web site: www.americanbookcompany.com

ACKNOWLEDGEMENTS

The authors would like to gratefully acknowledge the formatting and technical contributions of Becky Wright.

We also want to thank Mary Stoddard for her expertise in developing the graphics for this book.

We would also like to thank Phil Lausier for allowing us use of his nature photographs found in this book.

A special thanks to Marsha Torrens for her editing assistance.

This product/publication includes images from CorelDRAW 9 and 11 which are protected by the copyright laws of the United States, Canada and elsewhere. Used under license.

Table of Contents

Preface

The Georgia 7th Grade CRCT Test in Science will help students who are learning or reviewing material for the Georgia test that is now required for each gateway or benchmark course. **The materials in this book are based on the Georgia Performance Standards as published by the Georgia Department of Education.**

This book contains several sections. These sections are as follows: 1) General information about the book; 2) A Diagnostic Test and Evaluation Chart; 3) Domains/Chapters that teach the concepts and skills that improve readiness for Georgia 7th grade CRCT test in Science; 4) Two Practice Tests. Answers to the tests and exercises are in a separate manual. The answer manual also contains a Chart of Standards for teachers to make a more precise diagnosis of student needs and assignments.

We welcome comments and suggestions about the book. Please contact us at

American Book Company
PO Box 2638
Woodstock, GA 30188-1383

Toll Free: 1 (888) 264-5877
Phone: (770) 928-2834
Fax: (770) 928-7483
Web site: www.americanbookcompany.com

About the Author

Michelle Gunter graduated from Kennesaw State University in Kennesaw, Georgia with a B.S. in Secondary Biology Education. She is a certified teacher in the field of Biology in the state of Georgia. She has three years experience in high school science classrooms. She has six years experience in biology and biological systems. She has won awards for her research in the field of aquatic toxicology.

PREPARE FOR YOUR END OF COURSE AND EXIT EXAMS!

Let us Diagnose your needs and Provide instruction with our EASY TO USE books!

Through a unique partnership with **TutorVisa**, American Book Company now offers a **Diagnostic Test** that students can take **On-Line**. Test results are e-mailed to the teacher and the student and are graded with references to chapters in our book that will help reinforce the areas that are missed. It's 100% free, it takes the work out of hand grading, and it provides a specific prescription for improving students' performance on state and national assessments.

SIMPLY FOLLOW THESE 3 STEPS:

1. Teachers, provide students with the book's ISBN number and your e-mail address. Then have them go to **www.americanbookcompany.com/tutorvista** and take the FREE On-Line Diagnostic Test.

2. Teachers, determine the best way to use the Diagnostic Test results for your students and classes.

3. Students can use their FREE 2 HOUR TutorVista session to address specific needs and maximize their learning.

We are very excited about this new avenue for test preparation and hope you join us in this opportunity to improve student learning. If you have any questions about TutorVista or the processes explained above, please feel free to contact a customer representative by e-mail at **info@tutorvista.com** or by phone at **1-866-617-6020**.

You may also go to **www.americanbookcompany.com/tutorvista/diagnostic** for ideas and suggestions on how to effectively use this service for students and schools.

PO Box 2638 ★ Woodstock, GA 30188-1383 ★ Phone: 1-888-264-5877 ★ Fax: 1-866-827-3240
Web Site: www.americanbookcompany.com ★ E-mail: contact@americanbookcompany.com

Georgia 7th CRCT Diagnostic Test

Diagnostic Test   **Answer Sheet**

Name: _____

Section 1

1. (A) (B) (C) (D)
2. (A) (B) (C) (D)
3. (A) (B) (C) (D)
4. (A) (B) (C) (D)
5. (A) (B) (C) (D)
6. (A) (B) (C) (D)
7. (A) (B) (C) (D)
8. (A) (B) (C) (D)
9. (A) (B) (C) (D)
10. (A) (B) (C) (D)
11. (A) (B) (C) (D)
12. (A) (B) (C) (D)
13. (A) (B) (C) (D)
14. (A) (B) (C) (D)
15. (A) (B) (C) (D)
16. (A) (B) (C) (D)
17. (A) (B) (C) (D)
18. (A) (B) (C) (D)
19. (A) (B) (C) (D)
20. (A) (B) (C) (D)
21. (A) (B) (C) (D)

22. (A) (B) (C) (D)
23. (A) (B) (C) (D)
24. (A) (B) (C) (D)
25. (A) (B) (C) (D)
26. (A) (B) (C) (D)
27. (A) (B) (C) (D)
28. (A) (B) (C) (D)
29. (A) (B) (C) (D)
30. (A) (B) (C) (D)

Section 2

31. (A) (B) (C) (D)
32. (A) (B) (C) (D)
33. (A) (B) (C) (D)
34. (A) (B) (C) (D)
35. (A) (B) (C) (D)
36. (A) (B) (C) (D)
37. (A) (B) (C) (D)
38. (A) (B) (C) (D)
39. (A) (B) (C) (D)
40. (A) (B) (C) (D)

41. (A) (B) (C) (D)
42. (A) (B) (C) (D)
43. (A) (B) (C) (D)
44. (A) (B) (C) (D)
45. (A) (B) (C) (D)
46. (A) (B) (C) (D)
47. (A) (B) (C) (D)
48. (A) (B) (C) (D)
49. (A) (B) (C) (D)
50. (A) (B) (C) (D)
51. (A) (B) (C) (D)
52. (A) (B) (C) (D)
53. (A) (B) (C) (D)
54. (A) (B) (C) (D)
55. (A) (B) (C) (D)
56. (A) (B) (C) (D)
57. (A) (B) (C) (D)
58. (A) (B) (C) (D)
59. (A) (B) (C) (D)
60. (A) (B) (C) (D)

1. Consider the two lab setups S7CS2a, S7CS2c shown below. Which of the following answer choices correctly describes the lab setups?

A. The student in lab setup A is appropriately following lab safety precautions.

B. The student in lab setup B is appropriately following lab safety precautions.

C. The students in lab setup A and lab setup B are both following lab safety precautions.

D. There are no lab safety precautions when using Bunsen burners and test tubes.

2. Karen wants to win a blue ribbon at S7CS6 the fair this year for the largest tomato plants. She has devised an experiment that will compare two new plant foods, and help her determine which one makes her tomato plants grow larger.

She has three of the same type of tomato plants. They all receive the same amount of sunlight, water and temperature. Karen adds plant food A to Plant A, she adds plant food B to Plant B and she lets Plant C grow without any plant food. She measures the growth of the plants every week.

At the end of her experiment she has the following results:

	Week 1	Week 2	Week 3	Week 4
Plant A	2.3 cm	4.6 cm	6.1 cm	8.9 cm
Plant B	1.4 cm	2.8 cm	7.4 cm	9.6 cm
Plant C	1.0 cm	3.5 cm	6.6 cm	8.6 cm

A graph of her data might look similar to

A.

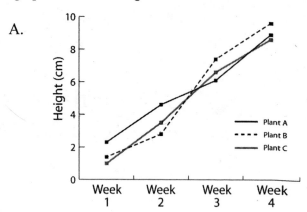

B.

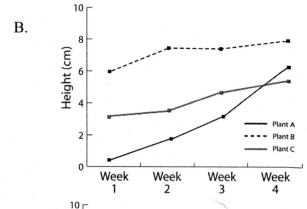

C.

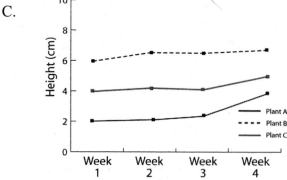

D.

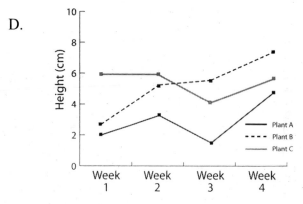

Please go on to the next page

Answer question 3 based on the summary of the following experiment.

A group of students investigated how temperature affects the rate of chemical reactions. They used hydrogen peroxide, which breaks down into oxygen and water, for their experiment. The students measured how long it took to obtain 50 mL of oxygen gas from a given volume of hydrogen peroxide heated to different temperatures. Their data are shown in the table below.

Temperature (°C)	Time (minutes)
10	33
20	16
30	8
40	4
50	2

3. Select the best way for the students to reduce the experimental error in their investigation.   S7CS9b

A. test more than one variable at a time

B. perform repeated trials

C. change their answers if they do not match their hypothesis

D. perform the experiment only one time

4. Genetic variation gives _____ to species and can increase their chance for survival.   S7L3b

A. similarity   C. variety

B. likeness   D. stability

5. The table shown presents data from an experiment that examined the effect of incubation temperatures on (a) the sex of the baby turtles that hatched and (b) the number of eggs that hatched.   S7CS9b

Group	Temperature °C	Number of Eggs	Number of Hatchlings		
			Male	Female	Total
1	26	25	19	2	21
2	28	25	14	9	23
3	30	25	4	16	20
4	32	25	2	22	24

Select the best conclusion about incubation temperatures above 29°C.

A. more eggs hatch

B. fewer eggs hatch

C. more male than female turtles hatch

D. fewer male than female turtles hatch

6. What is the piece of equipment shown below known as?   S7CS4b

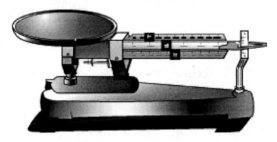

A. masstromoter

B. thermometer

C. triple beam balance

D. erlenmeyer flask

Use images below to answer question 7.

African Elephant   Asian Elephant

7. Which question below would be MOST useful when developing a dichotomous key to classify the animals seen here?   S7L1a

   A. Does the animal have large ears?
   B. Does the animal have tusks?
   C. Does the animal have a trunk?
   D. Does the animal have skin with little hair?

8. Meiosis is important to species reproduction because it promotes   S7L2b

   A. genetic variation.
   B. genetic mutations.
   C. fertilization.
   D. evolution.

9. In Hudson Bay, summer has arrived earlier each year since 1981. As a result, polar bears in that area have fewer offspring, and lower survival rates. This population has a   S7L4c

   A. positive growth rate.
   B. negative growth rate.
   C. stable growth rate.
   D. density dependent growth rate.

10. Consider the reactions shown below. Which of the following statements is NOT true concerning these reactions?   S7L2d

$$6\,CO_2 + 6\,H_2O + \text{light energy} \rightarrow C_6H_{12}O_6 \text{ (glucose)} + 6\,O_2$$

$$C_6H_{12}O_6 \text{ (glucose)} + 6\,O_2 \rightarrow 6\,CO_2 + 6\,H_2O + \text{energy}$$

   A. Photosynthesis converts solar energy into chemical energy.
   B. Sugar is a product of photosynthesis and a reactant in respiration.
   C. Photosynthesis is an endothermic reaction, and respiration is an exothermic reaction.
   D. Molecular oxygen is a reactant in photosynthesis and is a product of respiration.

11. In some fruit flies, the allele for having black eyes (B) is dominant to the allele for having red eyes (b). A scientist mated a batch of fruit flies with genotypes as shown in the Punnett Square below. What is the probability that the offspring will be born with red eyes?   S7L3a

	B	b
B	BB	Bb
b	Bb	bb

   A. 25%
   B. 75%
   C. 50%
   D. 100%

Please go on to the next page

12. When humans breed an organism for a particular size, color or shape this is known as -   S7L3c

     A. inbreeding.

     B. co-evolution.

     C. natural selection.

     D. selective breeding.

13. The mouth, stomach, liver, small intestine and large intestine collectively constitute a(n)   S7L2c

     A. tissue.

     B. organ system.

     C. tissue system.

     D. multicellular organism.

14. If a freshwater plant is placed in a saltwater tank, what will most likely happen to the water inside the plant cells?   S7L2a

     A. Nothing. The amount of water inside the cell will remain the same and the cell will remain the same size.

     B. More water will be added to it and the cell will swell.

     C. The water will leave the cell by osmosis and the cell will shrink.

     D. Nothing. The amount of water inside the cell will remain the same, the amount of salt inside the cell will increase.

15. The digestive system interacts with the _____ system to bring nutrients to cells.   S7L2e

     A. nervous   C. skeletal

     B. circulatory   D. excretory

Use the following image to answer questions 16 – 17.

16. How does the energy move between the deer, grass and buzzard?   S7L4a

     A. The grass traps energy from the Sun, the deer consumes the grass; when the deer dies, the buzzard consumes the deer.

     B. The deer traps energy from the Sun, the deer consumes the grass; when the deer dies, the buzzard consumes the deer.

     C. The buzzard traps energy from the Sun, the deer consumes the buzzard; when the buzzard dies, the grass consumes the buzzard.

     D. The grass traps energy from the Sun, the buzzard consumes the grass; when the buzzard dies, the deer consumes the buzzard.

17. Which organism shown in the image is a producer?   S7L4a

     A. deer

     B. grass

     C. buzzard

     D. all the organisms are producers

Use the following image to answer questions 18 – 19.

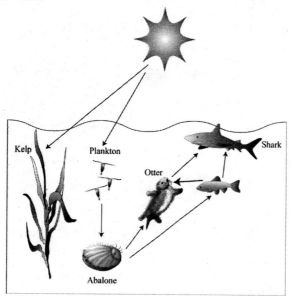

18. Which of the following organisms has   S7L4b
the most concentrated source of
energy contained within its tissues?

   A. shark

   B. otter

   C. abalone

   D. plankton

19. The image shows an example of a(n)   S7L4b

   A. food chain.

   B. food web.

   C. energy pyramid.

   D. trophic level.

20. An unusually harsh winter kills many   S7L4c
caribou in the Canadian arctic. This
type of limiting factor is known as a(n)

   A. density dependent.

   B. density independent.

   C. carrying capacity.

   D. density factor.

21. Some humans keep dogs as pets. The   S7L4d
dog receives a place to live and a
steady food supply. The human receives the
affection and interaction with the dog. This is
an example of

   A. mutualism.

   B. commensalism.

   C. parasitism.

   D. predator/prey.

22. A cell that has large vacuoles,   S7l2b
chloroplasts and a cell wall is probably a

   A. plant cell.

   B. animal cell.

   C. neither a plant or an animal cell.

   D. prokaryotic cell.

23. A biome found on either side of the   S7L4e
equator, between 0° and 20° latitude,
gets little rain and has extreme temperature
fluctuations. This is a description of the
biome's

   A. biotic factors.

   B. abiotic factors.

   C. salinity factors.

   D. average factors.

Please go on to the next page

24. An extinct north Atlantic bird called   S7L5b
the Great Auk looked very similar to
modern day penguins. However, the Great
Auk was not related to penguins. What
evolutionary idea explains how these two
unrelated species could develop similar
characteristics?

A. convergent evolution
B. divergent evolution
C. immigration
D. co-evolution

25. Which description below describes a   S7L4e
population?

A. a clearing in a forest
B. a temperate forest
C. a chipmunk (*Tamias sibiricus*)
D. a flock of wild turkeys (*Meleagris gallo-pavo*)

26. How did the Galapagos finches   S7L5a
change to fit the new environment?

A. All the finches in the population grew
new and different beak shapes.
B. Over many generations, the finches with
beak shapes suited to their environment and
food source, survived.
C. The finches chose to only produce offspring
that looked different from themselves.
D. The finches did not change to fit the new
environment.

27. The chemical energy supply for all   S7L2d
living cells is contained in a molecule
that, when broken down releases the energy
so that it may be used for activities such as
muscle contractions, photosynthesis and
locomotion. The molecule that is a
storehouse of energy is called

A. ATP.   C. RNA.
B. DNA.   D. ADP.

28. Examine the branching tree below.   S7L5a
Which two plants are the most closely
related?

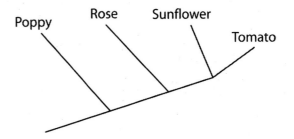

A. poppy and tomato
B. sunflower and poppy
C. rose and tomato
D. sunflower and tomato

29. Look at the image below. According to the picture, which statement is true?

S7L5c

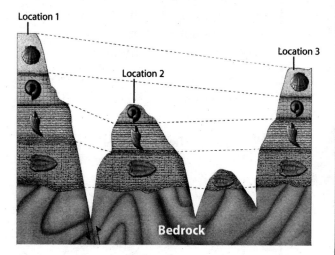

A. The fossils at the top of locations 1 and 3 are younger than the fossils at the top of location 2.

B. The fossils at the top of location 2 are younger than the fossils at the top of location 1 and 3.

C. The fossils at the top of locations 1 and 3 are the same age as the fossils at the top of location 2.

D. It is impossible to tell the relative age of the fossils with this picture.

30. What size is an ecosystem?

S7L4e

A. 10 square miles

B. 20 square miles

C. 100 square miles

D. varied sizes

DO **NOT** GO TO THE NEXT PAGE

Session 2

31. Which question would be LEAST useful when developing a dichotomous key to identify clothing? S7L1a

    A. What type of material is the clothing made of?
    B. Where is the clothing worn on the body?
    C. Is the clothing for a male or female?
    D. Is the clothing used to cover the body?

32. The Galapagos finches demonstrate what evolutionary idea? S7L5b

    A. convergent evolution
    B. divergent evolution
    C. artificial selection
    D. co-evolution

33. Bacteria live on the skin of humans. The bacteria receive food and shelter from human beings. Most bacteria are harmless and pose little or no threat to humans. This is an example of S7L4d

    A. mutualism.
    B. commensalism.
    C. parasitism.
    D. predator/prey.

34. Which two examples are the most general categories of living things? S7L1b

    A. diatoms and *E. coli*
    B. fungi and plantae
    C. amoeba and horse
    D. protista and tree

35. Organisms must show which of the following characteristics to be considered alive? S7L2a

    A. homeostasis, growth and reproduction only
    B. metabolism, reproduction, homeostasis, growth and sensitivity only
    C. metabolism, reproduction, homeostasis, growth, made of cells and sensitivity only
    D. metabolism, reproduction, homeostasis, growth, made of cells, adaptation and sensitivity

36. Why do scientists study taxonomy? S7L1b

    A. they like to know about taxes
    B. to make it easier to study living things
    C. to make it harder to study living things
    D. so they can use dichotomous keys

37. Use a Punnett Square to predict the cross of a homozygous striped parent with a homozygous solid parent if striped is dominant over solid. The phenotypes of the offspring will be S7L3a

    A. all striped.
    B. all solid.
    C. some striped and some solid.
    D. neither striped nor solid.

38. The tube that transports food from the mouth to the stomach is called S7L2e

    A. the gastric tube.
    B. the esophagus.
    C. the small intestine.
    D. the large intestine.

39. Which one of the following organisms would be considered a predator? S7L4a

    A. grass   C. caterpillar
    B. tree   D. tomato plant

Please go on to the next page   9

40. When humans alter the look or function of an organism over many successive generations they are practicing   S7L3c

   A. cloning.
   B. genetic engineering.
   C. inbreeding.
   D. selective breeding.

41. When plants or animals die, the matter that made up their bodies   S7L4a

   A. is destroyed by other animals.
   B. is destroyed by the sun.
   C. is recycled by other organisms.
   D. becomes pure energy.

42. The correct order of the cellular hierarchy from smallest to largest is   S7L2c

   A. cells-organs-tissues-organism-organisms.
   B. organs-organ systems-organisms-super organism.
   C. cells-organisms-tissues-organs.
   D. cells-tissues-organs-organ systems-organism.

43. What kind of organism is sometimes considered a primary consumer and sometimes considered a secondary consumer?   S7L4b

   A. producer   C. carnivore
   B. herbivore   D. omnivore

44. *Crotalus adamanteus* and *Crotalus horridus* are organisms that belong to the same   S7L1b

   A. population.   C. species.
   B. genus.   D. chromosome.

45. When a large tree in the rain forest falls, it creates a gap in the canopy. This opening allows sunlight to reach the forest floor. Many tree seedlings race upward to collect as much sunlight as possible. This is an example of what kind of species interaction?   S7L4d

   A. commensalism
   B. competition
   C. predator/prey
   D. parasitism

46. Prokaryotic cells have no   S7L2b

   A. nucleus.
   B. energy exchange.
   C. cell membrane.
   D. metabolism.

47. Why are fossils important to scientific thought?   S7L5c

   A. They provide evidence for the change seen in organisms over time.
   B. Because scientists like to dig in the dirt.
   C. They provide all knowledge about early Earth.
   D. Only fossils can date rock layers.

48. Somatic cells divide through   S7L3b

   A. mitosis.   C. cell intercycle.
   B. meiosis.   D. interphase.

49. Who proposed the theories on how organisms changed over time?   S7L5a

   A. Mendel
   B. Spallanzini
   C. Snow
   D. Darwin

Please go on to the next page

Use the graph to answer questions 50 – 51.

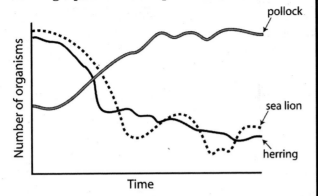

50. What type of species interaction is occurring between the herring and the sea lion?   S7L4d

    A. commensalism
    B. competition
    C. predator/prey
    D. parasitism

51. What type of species interaction is occurring between the herring and the pollock?   S7L4d

    A. commensalism
    B. competition
    C. predator/prey
    D. parasitism

52. For an ecosystem to succeed, it must accomplish which two main tasks?   S7L4e

    A. have both biotic and abiotic components
    B. recycle matter and have biotic components that trap and store energy
    C. have breeding species of plants and animals and good population interactions
    D. use inorganic chemicals to sustain live and breeding animal species

53. Which kind of organism has the most concentrated energy?   S7L4b

    A. dog   C. shark
    B. lion   D. alga

54. What is the process by which organisms naturally change over time called?   S7L5a

    A. commensalism
    B. evolution
    C. selective breeding
    D. osmosis

55. On a family vacation, a child observed clams, crabs, barnacles, starfish, gulls and sand pipers (birds). What ecosystem zone was this family visiting?   S7L4e

    A. the benthic zone
    B. the freshwater river zone
    C. the intertidal zone
    D. the pelagic zone

56. What animal populations described below would be considered at risk for a bottleneck?   S7L5b

    A. a large population of wildebeests
    B. an abundant type of sponge found on a coral reef
    C. a common type of house fly
    D. an endangered Indian tiger

57. Humans transport goldfinches from the northern United States to the southern United States. These new finches begin breeding with native goldfinch populations. The offspring of these two finch species show characteristics from both finch populations. What is this type of change in gene frequency called?   S7L5b

    A. mutation
    B. gene flow
    C. genetic drift
    D. bottlenecking

58. The fruit fly population in a particular orchard has many members. Each female fly lays many eggs over the course of her 30-day lifespan. If the environment changed quickly, how would the fruit fly population likely be affected?

A. The fruit fly population would adapt quickly to the change and survive.

B. The fruit fly population would not adapt at all to the change and would become extinct.

C. The fruit fly population would not adapt at all to the change and would survive.

D. The fruit fly population would adapt to the change and would become extinct.

59. What type of particle is used in radiometric dating of rock layers?   S7L5c

A. elementary

B. radioactive

C. neutron

D. proton

60. The graph below represents which type of growth rate?   S7L4c

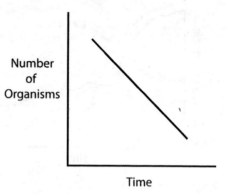

A. positive

B. negative

C. carrying capacity

D. limiting co-factor

DO **NOT** GO TO THE NEXT PAGE

EVALUATION CHART FOR GEORGIA 7TH GRADE CRCT TEST

Directions: On the following chart, circle the question numbers that you answered incorrectly, and evaluate the results. These questions are based on the Georgia Performance Standards for Science. Then turn to the appropriate topics (listed by chapters), read the explanations and complete the exercises. Review other chapters as needed. Finally, complete the practice test(s) to assess your progress and further prepare you for the *Georgia 7th Grade CRCT Test*.

*Note: Some question numbers will appear under multiple chapters because those questions require demonstration of multiple skills.

Chapters	Diagnostic Test Question
1. Making and Using a Dichotomous Key	7, 31
2. Six Kingdoms — Taxonomy	34, 36, 44
3. Cells and Cellular Transport	14, 35
4. Cellular Parts	8, 22, 46
5. Cellular Hierarchy	13, 42
6. Cellular Needs	10, 27
7. The Human Body	15, 38
8. Genetics and Chromosomes	11, 37
9. Sexual and Asexual Reproduction in Living Things	4, 48
10. Getting Desired Traits	12, 40
11. Food Webs Matter	16, 17, 39, 41
12. Transfer of Energy	18, 19, 43, 53
13. Environment and Organisms	9, 20, 58, 60
14. Organism Relationships	21, 33, 45, 50, 51
15. Earth's Biomes	23, 25, 30, 52, 55
16. Physical Change	26, 28, 49, 54
17. Natural Selection	24, 32, 56, 57
18. Fossil Record	29, 47, 59
Review co-requisite covered in Middle School Science	1, 2, 3, 5, 6

Chapter 1
Making and Using a Dichotomous Key

GEORGIA 7TH GRADE CRCT IN SCIENCE STANDARDS COVERED IN THIS CHAPTER INCLUDE:

S7L1a	Demonstrate the process for the development of a dichotomous key.

CLASSIFICATION

Have you ever helped put away the groceries? Or helped do the laundry? If you have, you might have noticed that things in your home are all grouped together in different locations. The cheese is kept in the refrigerator while a can of corn is in the pantry. Your shirts are in a drawer separate from your socks. Grouping similar things together makes it easier to live in the house. Grouping similar things together is called **classifying**. Scientists classify things to make them easier to study, observe and write about. The classification of living things is known as **taxonomy**.

When identifying living things, scientists use a tool called a dichotomous key. A **dichotomous key** is a series of paired choices that eventually identifies the plant, animal or object.

For example, when putting away the groceries with a dichotomous key, you might use the following pair of choices to help determine where the food will go:

1. Does the food need to be kept cold?

a. Yes
b. No

The answer to this general question helps you determine your next step. Later on, the unique characteristics of the object will be useful in determining the final steps of the classification. When making a dichotomous key, it is important to remember both the general and specific characteristics of the objects or organisms.

First, we must decide what general characteristic we want to use to divide the large group into smaller groups. Next, we must develop pairs of choices that narrow down the smaller groups into specific objects or organisms. Some keys are long and some are short — it depends on how many different items need to be classified, and how different they are.

Let's keep putting away the groceries and develop our own dichotomous key for putting away food.

For our first choice, we will use the broadest and most general characteristic of the objects. In the example above, we used temperature of the food. The next choices will be increasingly more specific, until we determine where all the food goes.

1. Does the food need to be kept cold?
a. Yes   Go to 2
b. No   Go to 3

2. Does the food need to be frozen?
a. Yes   Place in freezer
b. No   Go to 5

3. Does the food come in a can?
a. Yes   Place with other canned foods
b. No   Go to 4

4. Is the food used in baking?
a. Yes   Place with other baking goods
b. No   Place on pantry shelves.

5. Is the food a fresh fruit or vegetable?
a. Yes   Place in crisper
b. No   Place on refrigerator shelves

This key could be a lot longer, depending on how organized your kitchen is. Make your own dichotomous key for putting away groceries at your house.

Activity

Develop a dichotomous key using the following items: blue jeans, dress pants, plaid skirt and jogging shorts. Then select an item and use the key to determine if your key works. If it doesn't, revise your key and try again.

Activity

You just got your first job working at Sal's department store. Sal's department store carries electronics, items for the home, clothing, automotive, jewelry, cosmetics, exercise equipment and appliances. Write a dichotomous key to help you determine where to stock items returned by customers. Then select an item and use the key to determine if your key works. If it doesn't, revise your key and try again.

DICHOTOMOUS KEYS WITH LIVING THINGS

Now that you've had some experience making your own dichotomous key with familiar objects, let's try using one that contains living things. Dichotomous keys are very useful to scientists when they are attempting to identify an unknown plant or animal. Use the key on the next page to identify familiar animals into specific taxonomic groups (different taxonomic groups will be discussed in the next chapter). Pick an organism and follow the key to determine its correct classification.

1. Does the organism have an exoskeleton?

    a. Yes... Go to 2.

    b. No... Go to 4.

2. Does the organism have 8 legs?

    a. Yes. ...It is of Order Araneae.

    b. No. ...Go to 3.

3. Does the organism dwell exclusively on land?

    a. Yes... It is of Order Isapoda.

    b. No... Go to 4.

4. Does the organism have an endoskeleton?

    a. Yes...Go to 5.

    b. No... Go to 6.

5. Does the organism live only in the water?

    a. Yes...Go to 6

    b. No... Go to 7

6. Does the organism have stinging tentacles?

    a. Yes... It is of Phylum Cndaria.

    b. No... Go to 7.

7. Does the organism have 5 legs?

    a. Yes... It is of Phylum Echinodermata.

    b. No... Go to 8.

8. Does the organism carry live young in a pouch?

    a. Yes... Go to 9.

    b. No... Go to 10.

9. Does it climb trees?

    a. Yes... It is of Suborder Vombatiformes.

    b. No... It is of Suborder Phalangerida.

10. Is the organism a mammal?

    a. Yes.... Go to 11.

    b. No... It is of Order Perciformes.

11. Does the adult organism have teeth?

    a. Yes... It is of Suborder Odontoceti.

    b. No... It is of Suborder Mysticeti.

Activity

Develop a dichotomous key to identify different types of vertebrate animals, mammals, reptiles, flowering plants or trees.

Activity

Collect leaves from nearby trees and use a dichotomous key to identify the type of tree. The websites http://www.dnr.state.wi.us/org/caer/ce/eek/veg/treekey/ or http://www.arborday.org/trees/treeid.cfm are very useful when identifying common trees in Georgia.

Chapter 1 Review

1. Which of the following questions would be useful when developing a dichotomous key about the rabbits seen here?

   A. Does the rabbit have two eyes?

   B. Does the rabbit have four legs?

   C. Does the rabbit have long ears?

   D. Can the rabbit jump?

2. Taxonomy is

   A. the way animals group themselves in nature.

   B. the way scientists group living things.

   C. the way organs work together in an organism.

   D. useful only to scientists.

3. A dichotomous key

   A. is useful for identifying organisms.

   B. uses paired choices.

   C. can be long or short.

   D. all of the above

4. How many choices are used at each step in a dichotomous key?

   A. 1   B. 2   C. 3   D. 4

5. In which situation would a scientist use a dichotomous key?

   A. identifying the amount of pollution in a lake

   B. determining the tectonic shift along a plate boundary

   C. identifying an unknown flower

   D. identifying the amount of power used in a city

1.	Ⓐ	Ⓑ	Ⓒ	Ⓓ
2.	Ⓐ	Ⓑ	Ⓒ	Ⓓ
3.	Ⓐ	Ⓑ	Ⓒ	Ⓓ
4.	Ⓐ	Ⓑ	Ⓒ	Ⓓ
5.	Ⓐ	Ⓑ	Ⓒ	Ⓓ

Chapter 2
Six Kingdoms — Taxonomy

GEORGIA 7TH GRADE CRCT IN SCIENCE STANDARDS COVERED IN THIS CHAPTER INCLUDE:

S7L1b	Classify organisms based on a six-kingdom system and a dichotomous key.

BIOLOGICAL CLASSIFICATION

You are on a scientific mission in your local shoe store. There must be hundreds of shoes on the shelves — dress shoes, athletic shoes, work boots, western boots — and we haven't even begun to look at color and material. Your task: to classify all of the shoes into categories and sub-categories so that others can find the exact shoe you describe to them. How would you proceed? What general and specific categories would you establish? If you think THAT would be a difficult task, imagine changing the categorization topic to…every living thing on Earth! Scientists estimate that there may be up to 14 million different species inhabiting the planet. Approximately 1.75 million species have been scientifically named and described, including 250,000 plant species and 792,000 animal species. The variation among organisms is called **biodiversity**. It may seem to be a nearly impossible task, but believe it or not there is a system devised to organize all of those diverse organisms, and it works.

THE CURRENT VERSION OF THE HIERARCHY OF LIVING THINGS

Organisms are divided into several categories, based on a system that starts out broadly and becomes more specific. **Super kingdom** is the broadest category and includes the prokaryotes and the eukaryotes.

The **prokaryotes** are microscopic unicellular organisms that have a few organelles and no nucleus. They are mostly photosynthesizers or decomposers, but some are **pathogens,** or disease-causing. They are essential to the ecological well being of Earth. Prokaryotes are further divided into two kingdoms: **Eubacteria** and **Archaebacteria**.

The **eukaryotes** include both unicellular and multicellular organisms. Eukaryote means "**true kernel**" in Greek, with "kernel" representing the nucleus of the eukaryotic cell. Eukaryotes share an organized complex cellular structure, biochemistry and molecular biology. The eukaryotes are further divided into four kingdoms: Protista, Fungi, Plantae and Animalia.

Each kingdom further divides into **phylum** or **divisions**. The term "phyla" is used to name organisms in the kingdoms of Eubacteria, Archaeabacteria, Animalia, Protista, Fungi and Plantae. Phylum then break down into **classes**, and classes break down into **orders**. The categories become more detailed and include fewer organisms as they are further broken down into **family**, **genus** and species. The **species** is the most specific category.

To remember the order of the subdivisions, memorize the silly sentence:

"King Philip Came Over From Greece Speedily."

Occasionally you will see the terms sub-order or sub-family; these subdivisions seek to clarify digressions from the current taxonomy. That is part of the reason that this section is called "The Current Version…" Taxonomy changes in response to better information about an organism, better understanding of known information and discovery of new species. It is also possible that organisms may adapt and evolve to such an extent that their taxonomic classification must change.

Table 2.1

The Six Kingdoms			
Super Kingdom	**Kingdom**	**Basic Characteristic**	**Example**
Prokaryotes	Eubacteria	found everywhere	cynobacteria
	Archaebacteria	live without oxygen, get their energy from inorganic matter of light, found in extreme habitats	halophiles
Eukaryotes	Protista	one-celled or multicellular, true nucleus	amoeba
	Fungi	multicellular, food from dead organisms, cannot move	mushroom
	Plantae	multicellular, cannot move, make their own food, cell walls	tree
	Animalia	multicellular, moves about, depends on others for food	horse

These general categories are a good way to start the process of organization, but how about when we need to be more specific? **Carl Linnaeus** (1707 –1778), a Swedish botanist, devised the current system for classifying organisms. Linnaeus used **binomial nomenclature**, a system of naming organisms using a two-part name to label the species. The binomial name is written in Latin and is considered the **scientific name**. It consists of the generic name (**genus**) and the specific epithet (**species**). The entire scientific name is italicized, and the genus name is capitalized, as in *Homo sapiens* for humans.

Carl Linnaeus

One drawback to this system of classification is that it does not take into account the variation that exists among individuals within a species. All domestic dogs have the scientific name *Canis familiaris*, but a great deal of variation exists among different breeds of dogs and even among individual dogs of the same breed. Another drawback is that the most definitive test to determine if organisms are of the same species is to confirm their ability to breed successfully, producing fertile offspring. This is a problem in that controlled breeding of wild organisms for the purpose of observation and study can sometimes be impractical, if not impossible. In general, though, the Linnean system works quite well.

Activity

To see the Linnean system in action, check out the online encyclopedia, Wikipedia. Type in the name of any animal you want to learn more about. Try dolphin, which is in the sub-order Odontoceti, which contains all of the toothed whales. Can you think of a whale with teeth? Type its name in. Check that it is in the same sub-order as the dolphin, but in a different family. Why?

Chapter 2 Review

1. Which of the following group of categories is listed from broadest to most specific?

   A. family, order, class

   B. phylum, class, kingdom

   C. order, family, genus

   D. genus, family, species

2. The two-part system used to name organisms is called

   A. dual identification.

   B. binomial nomenclature.

   C. double nomenclature.

   D. Linnean nomenclature.

3. How many kingdoms are there in the current classification system?

   A. 4   B. 5   C. 6   D. 7

4. The eastern chipmunk is known to scientists as *Tamias striatus*. *Tamias striatus* is the _____ and _____ of this animal.

   A. genus, species

   B. family, species

   C. family, genus

   D. kingdom, order

5. Who developed the current system for classifying organisms?

   A. Charles Darwin

   B. Carl Linnaeus

   C. Theodor Schwann

   D. Matthias Schleiden

1. Ⓐ Ⓑ Ⓒ Ⓓ
2. Ⓐ Ⓑ Ⓒ Ⓓ
3. Ⓐ Ⓑ Ⓒ Ⓓ
4. Ⓐ Ⓑ Ⓒ Ⓓ
5. Ⓐ Ⓑ Ⓒ Ⓓ

Domain 1
Cells and Genetics

Chapter 3: Cells and Cellular Transport

S7L2a

This chapter discusses what characteristics all organisms share; viruses; cell theory and cellular transport.

Chapter 4: Cellular Parts

S7L2b

This chapter distinguishes between different types of cells and describes cellular organelles.

Chapter 5: Cellular Hierarchy

S7L2c

This chapter describes cells, tissues, organs and organ systems. Included in this chapter are examples at each level of organization.

Chapter 6: Cellular Needs

S7L2d

This chapter discusses the three main processes cells use to gather and convert energy: photosynthesis, respiration and fermentation. This chapter also discusses how tissues, organs and organ systems meet cellular needs.

Chapter 7: The Human Body

S7L2e

This chapter provides an overview of the systems found in the human body: circulatory, digestive, skeletal, respiratory, immune, lymphatic, muscular, nervous, excretory and reproductive.

Chapter 8: Genetics and Chromosomes

S7L3a

This chapter distinguishes between different types of inheritance: simple dominant/recessive, incomplete dominance and co-dominance. A sample Punnett Square is also described.

Chapter 9: Sexual and Asexual Reproduction

S7L3b

This chapter introduces the concepts of cell cycle, mitosis and meiosis. A brief overview of reproduction strategies in the six kingdoms is also given.

Chapter 10: Getting Desired Traits

S7L3c

This chapter discusses how humans have impacted organism traits through selective breeding. Topics such as inbreeding, hybridization, genetic engineering, mutations and cloning are covered.

Make a Concept Map

Use the blank space here to develop your own concept map about topics in Domain 1. Complete this activity **before** beginning the domain to find out what you may already know about cells and genetics! Then, at the end of the domain, return to your concept map and add or change things you learned in this section. Review **Appendix A** for directions on making concept maps.

Chapter 3
Cells and Cellular Transport

GEORGIA 7TH GRADE CRCT IN SCIENCE STANDARDS COVERED IN THIS CHAPTER INCLUDE:

S7L2a	Explain that cells take in nutrients in order to grow and divide and to make needed materials.

CHARACTERISTICS OF LIFE

Now that we have discovered the hierarchy of living things, it would be a good idea if we could all agree on what constitutes a living thing! *All* living things, also called **organisms**, share the following characteristics:

1. Cells

2. Sensitivity (response to stimuli)

3. Growth

4. Homeostasis (stable internal environment)

5. Reproduction

6. Metabolism (transformation and use of energy)

7. Adaptation

1. **Cells:** Cells make up all living things. Cells can sometimes organize into complex structures. Multicellular organisms have many cells and unicellular organisms have only one cell.

2. **Sensitivity:** Organisms respond to stimuli in the environment. A **stimulus** is a change in the environment. **Responses** are reactions to **stimuli** in the environment. Examples of responses to stimuli include a plant that grows toward a light source or an animal that flees from a predator. Responses occur many times in the life of one organism.

3. **Growth:** Organisms change over their lifetime. Organisms may develop new structures or behaviors as they age, and/or increase in size.

4. **Homeostasis:** Organisms must maintain an internal environment that is suitable for life. **Homeostasis** is the ability of an organism to keep a steady internal state. Living things need the correct amount of fluids, salts, hormones and food sources in order to survive.

5. **Reproduction:** All living things must be able to reproduce. Organisms can reproduce sexually or asexually. **Sexual reproduction** occurs when two organisms create offspring and **asexual reproduction** occurs when one organism is capable of creating offspring by itself.

6. **Metabolism:** Organisms must get energy from the environment and use the energy they obtain to live. **Metabolism** is the sum of all chemical reactions within a cell or organism as it acquires and processes nutrients to produce energy.

7. **Adaptation:** Over time, organisms can become specially suited to a particular environment. Sea turtles have long, flipper-like legs and cannot easily walk on land. They are adapted to living in the ocean. Adaptations occur slowly, over the course of many generations. Remember: *adaptations occur to populations of organisms, not to the individual organisms themselves.*

VIRUSES ARE DIFFERENT FROM LIVING THINGS

You've heard of the flu, haven't you? The flu is an illness, caused by the influenza virus, and easily passes from person to person. You may think a virus is a living thing because it can be transmitted by living things. But if you look at the characteristics and processes of living things, you'll have to agree that a virus is not a living thing. A virus particle cannot eat, and it can only reproduce inside a cell. Outside the cell, a virus particle does nothing and remains inactive. So what is it? A **virus** is a small particle that contains proteins and hereditary material (DNA or RNA), but it is not alive. The virus is surrounded by a protein coat, or **capsid**. Viruses are cell-specific, meaning they can only infect a cell if the capsid of the virus can fit into a receptor site in the host cell membrane.

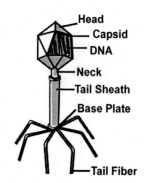

Figure 3.1 Virus Particle

CELL THEORY AND STRUCTURE

And now…back to the world of the living. What is the basic structural and functional unit of all organisms? Here's a hint: it's something that sounds confining, but is nonetheless greatly variable. If you guessed it was cells (and even if you didn't) then you are ready to read on. The **cell** is the basic structural and functional unit of all organisms. The cell theory is the basis for the way biologists study organisms and helps to differentiate living things from non-living things.

The **cell theory** states that:

- all living things are made of cells.
- all cells come from other living cells of the same kind.
- cells are the basic unit of all living things.

In addition, the cell is an organism unto itself. It can do all the things that other organisms can do, like eating and reproducing.

TRANSPORT

The process of transport describes the cell's ability to move materials around. There are two different mechanisms of transport: passive and active.

Passive transport is spontaneous (meaning it happens without any action on the part of the cell) and does not require energy. In passive transport, molecules move spontaneously through the plasma membrane from areas of higher concentration to areas of lower concentration. The two types of passive transport are **diffusion** and **osmosis.**

Diffusion is the process by which substances move from areas of higher concentration to areas of lower concentration.

Osmosis is the movement of water through a semi-permeable membrane from an area of high water concentration to an area of low water concentration. Sometimes a membrane, like a cell membrane, is **semi-permeable,** which means it prevents some molecules from crossing. Think of osmosis as the diffusion of water when only water can get through a semi-permeable membrane.

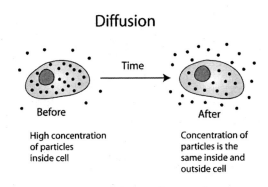

Diffusion

Before — High concentration of particles inside cell

After — Concentration of particles is the same inside and outside cell

Figure 3.2

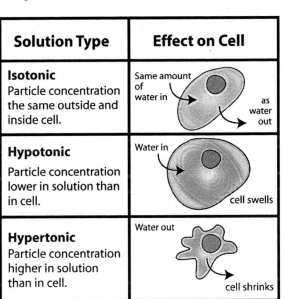

Solution Type	Effect on Cell
Isotonic Particle concentration the same outside and inside cell.	Same amount of water in as water out
Hypotonic Particle concentration lower in solution than in cell.	Water in — cell swells
Hypertonic Particle concentration higher in solution than in cell.	Water out — cell shrinks

Figure 3.3

Sometimes cells are placed in different types of solutions. The concentrations of particles in the solution and in the cell can cause the water to move across the cell membrane. The solutions are described by the amount of particles in solution compared to the amount of particles in the cell. The three types of solutions and their effects are listed in Figure 3.3.

Active Transport is not spontaneous. A cell must use stored energy to move substances across the cell membrane in the opposite direction of concentration. For example, using active transport, a cell will move dissolved substances from an area of lower concentration to an area of higher concentration. This movement is the opposite of diffusion and, therefore, requires energy.

Exocytosis is a type of active transport in which materials are discharged out of a cell. The opposite of exocytosis is **endocytosis,** a type of active transport in which substances are imported into the cell.

Activity
Open a container of perfume and place in one corner of the classroom. Predict the order in which students will begin to first detect the perfume smell.

Chapter 3 Review

1. According to the cell theory, all cells

    A. are eukaryotic.

    B. are prokaryotic.

    C. have nuclei.

    D. come from other cells.

2. The movement of substances into and out of a cell without the use of energy is called

    A. active transport.

    B. passive transport.

    C. exocytosis.

    D. endocytosis.

3. A type of membrane which allows only certain molecules to pass through is called

    A. permeable.

    B. semi-permeable.

    C. active.

    D. porous.

4. Two types of passive transport are

    A. diffusion and osmosis.

    B. diffusion and endocytosis.

    C. exocytosis and endocytosis.

    D. osmosis and endocytosis.

5. During active transport

    A. water moves passively through a membrane.

    B. the movement of particles occurs spontaneously in the opposite direction of concentration.

    C. cells must use stored energy to move substances across a membrane.

    D. cells allow the spontaneous movement of particles across the membrane.

1. Ⓐ Ⓑ Ⓒ Ⓓ
2. Ⓐ Ⓑ Ⓒ Ⓓ
3. Ⓐ Ⓑ Ⓒ Ⓓ
4. Ⓐ Ⓑ Ⓒ Ⓓ
5. Ⓐ Ⓑ Ⓒ Ⓓ

Chapter 4
Cellular Parts

GEORGIA 7TH GRADE CRCT IN SCIENCE STANDARDS COVERED IN THIS CHAPTER INCLUDE:

S7L2b	Relate cell structure (cell membrane, nucleus, cytoplasm, chloroplasts, mitochondria) to basic cell functions.

BASIC CELL STRUCTURE

Cells have three basic parts:

Cell membrane	The cell membrane is the thin flexible boundary surrounding the cell.
Cytoplasm	The cytoplasm is the watery, jelly-like part of the cell that contains salts, minerals and the cell organelles.
Genetic material	The genetic material is the area of the cell where the DNA (deoxyribonucleic acid) is stored. It regulates all the cellular activities.

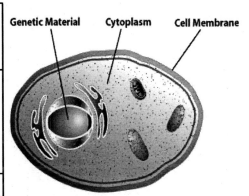

Figure 4.1 Basic Cell Structure

Organelles, or "little organs," are small, specialized cellular subunits separated from the rest of the cell by a membrane. Organelles help a cell to move molecules, create and store energy, store information and perform many other functions. Different kinds of cells have different organelles.

PROKARYOTIC VS. EUKARYOTIC CELLS

Remember the super kingdoms? There are two basic types of cells: prokaryotic and eukaryotic.

A **prokaryotic** *(pro-* before; *karyotic*-nucleus) cell does **not** have a true nucleus. Although the genetic material is usually contained in a central location, a membrane does not surround it. Furthermore, prokaryotic cells have no membrane-bound organelles. Prokaryotic cells are a more primitive type of cell: however, that doesn't mean it isn't resilient. **Bacteria** are prokaryotic, and they have been around a long time!

A **eukaryotic** *(eu-* true; *karyotic*- nucleus) cell has a nucleus surrounded by a nuclear membrane. It also has several membrane-bound organelles. Eukaryotic cells tend to be larger and more complex than prokaryotic cells. **Plant** and **animal** cells are both eukaryotic and, although similar in structure, contain unique cell parts. For instance, plant cells have a **cell wall** and **chloroplasts**, while some animal cells have **cilia** and **flagella**.

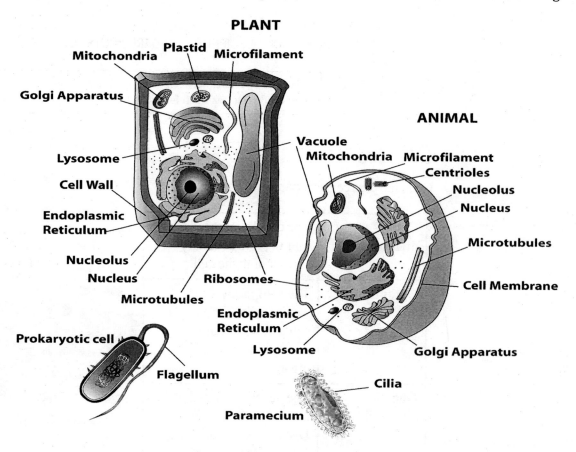

Figure 4.2 Plant and Animal Cellular Structures

BASIC CELL ORGANELLES

All this talk about cells and we still haven't looked at what they are made of. Look no further! On the next page you'll find a chart showing the main organelles that make up eukaryotic cells. Read the table several times to be sure you have a good basic understanding of the parts of cells. Pay particular attention to the organelles that are only in plant or animal cells. They are clues to an even more important understanding of how plants differ from animals in one important life process: the ability to make food.

Table 4.1 Parts of the Cell

Name	Description
Cell Wall (plant cells only)	Rigid membrane around plant cell; made of cellulose and provides shape and support
Plastids (plant cells only)	Group of structures (chloroplasts, leukoplasts, chromoplasts) used in photosynthesis and product storage; have a double membrane and provide color and cellular energy
Vacuoles	Spherical storage sac for food and water
Cell Membrane	Membrane surrounding the cell that allows some molecules to pass through
Golgi Bodies	Flattened membrane sacs for synthesis, packaging and distribution
Mitochondria	Rod-shaped double membranous structures where cellular respiration takes place
Endoplasmic Reticulum (ER)	Folded membranes having areas with and without ribosomes used for transport of RNA and proteins
Nucleus	Control center of the cell; location of hereditary information; surrounded by nuclear envelope
Ribosomes	Structures that make proteins; found on ER in the cytoplasm
Lysosomes	Spherical sac containing enzymes for digestive functions
Cilia (animal cell only)	Short, hair-like extensions on the surface of some cells used for movement and food gathering
Flagella (animal cell only)	Long, whip-like extension on the surface of some cells used for movement
Cytoplasm	Jelly-like substance in the cell around nucleus and organelles

Did you notice the differences? Plant and animal cells are both eukaryotic and, although similar in structure, contain unique cell parts. For one, you can see that plants have a cell *wall* and animals have a cell *membrane*. The **cell wall** is a rigid, sticky boundary that sticks to the cell walls of those cells adjacent to it; it also provides structure to the plant. The animal **cell membrane** is not a structural unit; its primary purpose is to regulate the transport of material into and out of the cell. In addition, cell membranes also surround the organelles in a cell and the nucleus. All these walls and membranes define and compartmentalize the cell. They serve to regulate the movement of almost everything — not just into and out of the cell, but within and between the parts of the cell's interior.

Activity

Make a model of a plant or animal cell using items found at home or school. Or draw and label parts of plant and animal cells on poster board and present to the class describing the shape and function of each organelle.

Chapter 4 Review

1. The mitochondrion of a cell

   A. has only one membrane.

   B. has no membrane.

   C. is circular.

   D. is where cellular respiration occurs.

2. Ribosomes

   A. are the site of protein synthesis.

   B. are made by other ribosomes.

   C. have their own DNA.

   D. none of the above

3. Structures that support and give shape to plant cells are

   A. microbodies.

   B. Golgi bodies.

   C. nucleus.

   D. cell walls.

4. The storage of hereditary information in a eukaryotic cell is in the

   A. cytoplasm.

   B. nucleus.

   C. centrioles.

   D. lysosomes.

5. Plastids are found

   A. only in plant cells.

   B. only in animal cells.

   C. in plant and animal cells.

   D. only in prokaryotic cells.

```
1. (A) (B) (C) (D)
2. (A) (B) (C) (D)
3. (A) (B) (C) (D)
4. (A) (B) (C) (D)
5. (A) (B) (C) (D)
```

Chapter 5
Cellular Hierarchy

GEORGIA 7TH GRADE CRCT IN SCIENCE STANDARDS COVERED IN THIS CHAPTER INCLUDE:

S7L2c	Explain that cells are organized into tissues, tissues into organs, organs into systems and systems into organisms.

CELLULAR HIERARCHY

In Chapter 4 you learned about the structure of plant and animal cells. How does this relate to actual plants and animals? As you may have guessed, the cellular hierarchy starts with one cell and works its way up to ever more complex cell groups that eventually form the most complex of living things. Take a look at the diagram and you should recognize most of the words, because they relate to cell systems within the human body.

Cellular Hierarchy

Cells ——▶ Tissues ——▶ Organs ——▶ Organ systems ——▶ Organism

Some organisms are **unicellular**, meaning they have only one cell. For example, bacteria and amoebas are unicellular. The single cell carries out all life functions.

Multicellular organisms are composed of many cells that work together to carry out life processes. In multicellular organisms, the cells group together and divide the labor.

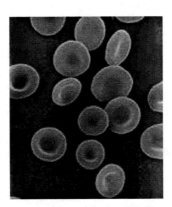

Figure 5.1 Red Blood Cells

Cells in a multicellular organism become specialized to perform specific functions. These specializations usually cause the cells in a multicellular organism to take on special shapes. For example, nerve cells are long and have many finger-like extensions. This shape helps transmit information over long distances, throughout the body. Cells lining the respiratory system have many cilia attached to help filter incoming air and remove mucus. Cells lining the digestive tract have many folds to help absorb more nutrients during digestion. Some examples of cells are blood cells, nerve cells, liver cells, muscle cells and skin cells.

Cells group together to perform the same function and are called **tissues**. The human body is made up of four basic types of tissue: epithelial, connective, muscle and nervous. Epithelial tissue usually surrounds and protects the things beneath it. Epithelial tissue has cells close together and some examples are skin, ducts and tubes. Connective tissue connects and supports body parts. Cartilage and blood are two examples of connective tissue. Muscle tissue helps move the body. Muscle tissue moves bones, digestive organs and the heart. Nervous tissue carries messages from the body and environment to the brain.

Several types of tissues group together and form an **organ**. The brain, heart, stomach and lungs are some examples of organs. Organs usually perform a complex task. For example, the stomach is an organ that chemically and mechanically digests food. The stomach is made up of several types of tissue, like epithelial tissue that lines the stomach, smooth muscle tissue that moves food through the stomach and nerve tissue that tells the brain when the stomach is full. All the different tissue types work together to digest food.

Several organs work together and make up an **organ system**. An **organ system** is a group of organs working together for a particular function. Examples of organ systems are the digestive system, circulatory system and nervous system. The organ systems of multicellular organisms work together to carry out the life processes of the organism, with each system performing a specific function. The organelles in unicellular organisms work like the organ systems of multicellular organisms. Each organelle has a specific function to keep the one-celled organism alive.

All the organ systems combine to make up the organism.

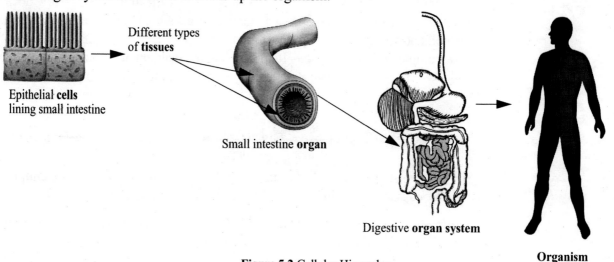

Epithelial **cells** lining small intestine

Different types of **tissues**

Small intestine **organ**

Digestive **organ system**

Organism

Figure 5.2 Cellular Hierarchy

Table 5.1 Some Examples in the Cellular Hierarchy

Examples of **Tissues**	Examples of **Organs**	Examples of **Organ Systems**
epithelial	skin	integumentary system
nerve	brain	nervous system
connective	heart	circulatory system
muscle	biceps brachii	muscular system

As living things become more complex, their cells become more specialized into specific types of tissues and organs. This differentiation takes place as the organism is first developed and keeps happening as cells must be replaced. It is *how* an organism's cells are differentiated into specialized tissue, organs and organ systems during the initial developmental period that determines what kind of living thing the organism will become.

Activity

Use encyclopedias, medical dictionaries or the internet to research the following body parts. Classify each as a/an **organelle**, **cell**, **tissue**, **organ** or **organ system**.

stomach, teeth, peripheral nervous system, gluteus maximus, femoral artery, leukocytes, aorta, esophagus, tongue, adrenal glands, pericardium, latissimus dorsi, neuron, ganglion, liver, sternum, tendon, duodenum, ribcage, amygdala, spinal cord and chloroplast.

Use the table below to help you. The first one is done for you.

Part	Type	Function
stomach	organ	to digest food

Chapter 5 Review

1. A(n) _____ is a group of different tissues that work together to perform a certain function.

    A. organ system

    B. organ

    C. cell

    D. organelle

2. Your heart functions through the use of several tissues like cardiac muscle, blood and connective tissues. Your heart is considered a(n)

    A. organ system.

    B. organ.

    C. cell.

    D. organelle.

3. The central nervous system (CNS) is made up of the brain and spinal cord. The CNS is a(n)

    A. organ system.

    B. organ.

    C. cell.

    D. organelle.

4. Which of the following is listed from least to most complex?

    A. organ, organism, cells

    B. cells, tissues, organism, organ system

    C. cells, organ, organism

    D. tissues, organism, organ

5. Which of the following is an example of a tissue?

    A. chloroplast

    B. stomach

    C. human

    D. bone

1.	Ⓐ	Ⓑ	Ⓒ	Ⓓ
2.	Ⓐ	Ⓑ	Ⓒ	Ⓓ
3.	Ⓐ	Ⓑ	Ⓒ	Ⓓ
4.	Ⓐ	Ⓑ	Ⓒ	Ⓓ
5.	Ⓐ	Ⓑ	Ⓒ	Ⓓ

Chapter 6
Cellular Needs

S7L2d	Explain that tissues, organs and organ systems serve the needs cells have for oxygen, food and waste removal.

PHOTOSYNTHESIS AND CELLULAR RESPIRATION

Remember that one organelle that distinguishes between plant and animal cells is the **plastid**. THINK QUICKLY: Do plant or animal cells have plastids? OK, if you said plant cells, you are right! Plant cells have plastids, and one kind of plastid is the **chloroplast**, which is where photosynthesis takes place. You see, green plants make their own food in a process called **photosynthesis**. The green pigment in plants uses sunlight, carbon dioxide from the air, along with water taken in through the roots of the plant and changes them into food. This **food** is stored in the plant as **glucose**, which is a form of **sugar**. Think of glucose/sugar as concentrated energy. Here's what photosynthesis looks like in formula form:

PHOTOSYNTHISIS

$$\text{Carbon Dioxide} + \text{Water} \xrightarrow[\text{Light Energy}]{\text{in the presence of}} \text{Glucose} + \text{Oxygen}$$

Photosynthesis converts light energy to food. Only plant cells can make their own food by converting energy in this way. However, all biological organisms obtain food. But what for? Think about the last time you were hungry. Were you tired, dragging your heels? You said you had no *energy*. Well, you were right! Here is the relationship:

NO FOOD = NO ENERGY!

Organisms need and use energy for everything: moving, making protein, getting rid of wastes, growing and repairing cell damage. Most plants and animals get their energy through the process of **respiration**, which takes place in the **mitochondria** of the cell (take another look at the cell diagrams). Animals take in food and break it down through digestion. After digestion, the nutrients are carried by the blood cells where cellular respiration takes place. In the process of **cellular respiration**, adenosine triphosphate (**ATP**) stores energy and controls the release of energy in the cell. ATP is a coenzyme composed of a base, a sugar and three phosphate groups. For our purposes, we'll just consider ATP to *be* energy, even though we know that it's much more complicated than that. Here's what the cellular respiration process looks like in formula form:

RESPIRATION

Glucose + Oxygen $\xrightarrow[\text{(in the presence of enzymes)}]{\text{YIELDS}}$ Carbon Dioxide + Water + ATP

(energy)

Take a look at both formulas and what do you notice? Look closely and you'll see they are exact opposites! In photosynthesis, energy is used to produce food; in respiration, food is used to produce energy.

ANAEROBIC RESPIRATION

Anaerobic respiration, or fermentation, is the process by which sugars break down in the absence of oxygen. Animal muscle cells, fungi and some bacteria are capable of carrying out anaerobic respiration.

Have you ever sprinted really fast? If you have, you might have noticed a burning sensation in your leg muscles. This burning is because your leg muscles are using up oxygen faster than your respiratory and circulatory systems can replace it. Your leg muscles begin to produce lactic acid in a process called lactic acid fermentation. Your muscle cells do this to get the energy needed to keep moving.

Yeast and some bacteria can carry out alcoholic fermentation. Carbon dioxide gas is released during alcohol fermentation. Yeast is commonly put in bread to make it rise. The fermentation of the yeast produces carbon dioxide, which becomes trapped in the dough, forming small bubbles and causing the bread to rise.

CHEMOSYNTHESIS

Chemosynthesis is the process by which inorganic chemicals are broken down to release energy. The only known organisms that are able to carry out chemosynthesis are bacteria. These organisms form the base of the food chain around thermal vents found on the ocean floor. They may also be found around other aquatic volcanic vents like those around Yellowstone National Park.

Chemosynthetic bacteria are also an important part of the nitrogen cycle. Some of these bacteria have adapted to conditions that would have existed on the early Earth, leading some scientists to hypothesize that these are actually living representatives of the earliest life on Earth.

TISSUES, ORGANS AND ORGAN SYSTEMS MEET CELLULAR NEEDS

As you have learned, cells need nutrients and energy to survive. In multicellular organisms, specialized cells carry out specific tasks. All cells, including specialized ones, need an input of nutrients and a removal of wastes to survive.

Think of it like a family. Each member of the family has a specialized function, one member goes grocery shopping and cooks the meals, one member does the laundry, one member cleans the house and takes out the trash and one member earns the money. Although each member has a specific function, they all need energy, clean clothes, clean environment and money.

Cells in a multicellular organism are similar. The digestive system provides nutrients and energy; the circulatory system transports nutrients, energy and wastes; the respiratory system provides oxygen; the excretory system removes the wastes; the muscular system moves the organism; the skeletal system supports the organism; the immune system protects the organism from disease; and the nervous system sends messages.

Imagine for a minute that you were a liver cell. Your job would be to filter out waste products. You would use active transport to do your job. Where would you get the energy? That's right, from cellular respiration. Where would you get your nutrients needed to carry out respiration? That's right, from the organ systems. The respiratory system would take in the necessary oxygen, while the circulatory system would transport the oxygen to you. The digestive system would bring you the necessary glucose and the nervous system would tell you when to do your job and what wastes you needed to remove. Finally the excretory system would carry away the waste products you filtered out. In this way the tissues, organs and organ systems work together to meet the needs of the cell and the organism.

Activity

Use the following materials to make a leaf print from pigments already contained within the leaf. A block of wood, thumbtacks, white fabric, a hammer and a fresh green leaf. Thumb tack the piece of white cloth over the leaf on the block of wood. Be sure the cloth is tight. Gently use the hammer to beat the fabric over the leaf to break open the cells and chloroplasts. To make the print last, mist with vinegar and press with a hot iron. You can also try this activity with autumn leaves harvested in early autumn before they fall from the tree. Predict what types of leaves will give the best results. As an extension, use dead leaves collected from the ground. Predict if these leaves will make good prints.

Chapter 6 Review

1. What is the chemical form of energy used by cells?

   A. enzymes

   B. cofactors

   C. ATP

   D. DNA

2. The process of releasing energy from the chemical breakdown of compounds in a cell is

   A. hesitation.

   B. expiration.

   C. elimination.

   D. respiration.

3. In photosynthesis, plants use carbon dioxide, water and light to produce

   A. carbon monoxide.

   B. energy.

   C. glucose and oxygen.

   D. chlorophyll.

4. Photosynthesis takes place inside

   A. mitochondria.

   B. chloroplasts.

   C. animal cells.

   D. none of the above

5. Ultimately the energy your body uses comes from

   A. the Sun.

   B. enzymes.

   C. expiration.

   D. the water cycle.

1.	Ⓐ	Ⓑ	Ⓒ	Ⓓ
2.	Ⓐ	Ⓑ	Ⓒ	Ⓓ
3.	Ⓐ	Ⓑ	Ⓒ	Ⓓ
4.	Ⓐ	Ⓑ	Ⓒ	Ⓓ
5.	Ⓐ	Ⓑ	Ⓒ	Ⓓ

Chapter 7
The Human Body

GEORGIA 7TH GRADE CRCT IN SCIENCE STANDARDS COVERED IN THIS CHAPTER INCLUDE:

S7L2e	Explain the role of the major organ systems in the human body.

If you think of the human body as a team, then the organ systems within it would be the players. This team must work together in order for you to maintain good health and *homeostasis*.

Were you surprised by the unfamiliar word? Here is the definition: **homeostasis** is the process of maintaining a fairly constant internal environment despite changing conditions; it is how we "regulate ourselves." Although you may not recall the word, you feel its effects every day. Here are a few examples:

- **Sweating** cools us and helps us maintain a constant internal temperature.
- We **drink water** to remain hydrated and maintain our body's water balance.
- We **excrete** toxic waste products to maintain a clean bloodstream.

To accomplish homeostasis, the combined efforts of cells, organs and organ systems are required. We won't look at every part of our "human body team," but we will examine several "star players."

Table 7.1 Overview of Human Body Systems

System	Major Parts and Organs
Circulatory	heart, veins, arteries and capillaries
Digestive	tongue, teeth, salivary glands, esophagus, stomach, pancreas, liver, gall bladder, small intestine, appendix and large intestine
Skeletal	skull, vertebral column, sternum, ribs, humerus, radius, ulna, carpals, metacarpals, phalanges, pelvic girdle, femur, patella, tibia, fibula, tarsals and metatarsals
Respiratory	nose, trachea, bronchial tubes, lungs, alveolus and diaphragm
Muscular	involuntary (smooth muscles), heart and voluntary (striated muscles)
Nervous	brain (cerebrum, medulla, cerebellum), spinal cord and nerve cells
Excretory	kidney, blood vessels, bladder, ureter, urethra, skin and sweat glands
Reproductive	male: testes, vas deferens, seminal vesicle, penis; female: ovary, oviduct, uterus, cervix and vagina

CIRCULATORY SYSTEM

The circulatory system is a transport system for many substances. It interacts with all other systems most notably the **digestive** and **respiratory** systems. The **heart** is the pump of the circulatory system, located between the lungs. It is a hollow muscular organ with four chambers that performs two primary functions.

- collects deoxygenated (without oxygen) blood from the body and pumps it to the lungs, and then…
- collects oxygenated blood from the lungs and pumps it throughout the body.

The respiratory system and circulatory system work closely together because your body needs to take in oxygen and send it to your cells.

Oxygenated blood has passed through the lungs to pick up oxygen, and is ready to travel through the body to deliver that oxygen to your cells. Blood that is **deoxygenated** has traveled through the body and has already delivered oxygen to your cells.

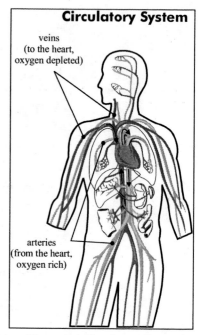

Figure 7.1 Circulatory System

DIGESTIVE SYSTEM

The **digestive system** breaks down food into smaller pieces that can be used by your cells. The digestive system is made up of several organs located in your mouth and inside your body. Some important organs involved in digestion include: esophagus, stomach, liver, small intestine and large intestine.

Digestion can happen two ways: mechanically and chemically. Mechanical digestion occurs when food is physically broken into smaller pieces. **Mechanical digestion** occurs when you chew your food, and during movement of the stomach. **Chemical digestion** happens when chemicals inside your body break down food. One example of chemical digestion is your stomach acid dissolving food. The digestive system works with the circulatory and excretory systems to bring nutrients to your cells and remove wastes.

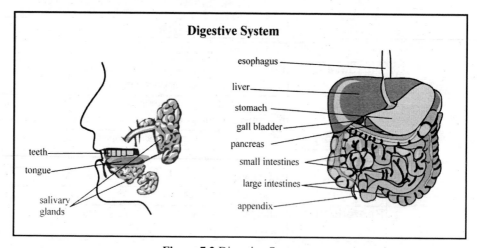

Figure 7.2 Digestive System

SKELETAL SYSTEM

The skeletal system is made up of bones, cartilage, tendons and ligaments. The skeletal system provides support and structure for the body mostly in the form of **bones**. Bones are a hard connective tissue composed mostly of calcium phosphate. Skeletal muscle attaches to bones to allow for movement. Bone is also a source of calcium for other organs in our bodies. Bone tissue renews itself periodically. When old bone breaks down, calcium and phosphorus are admitted into the bloodstream and are able to be used in other ways.

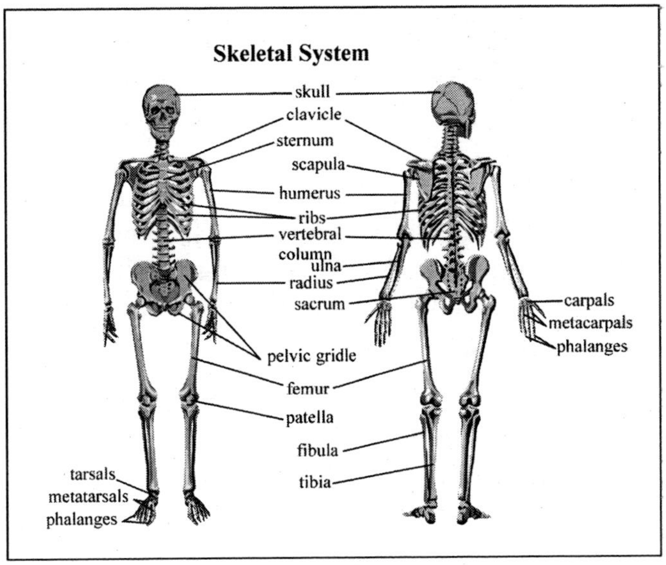

Skeletal System

skull
clavicle
sternum
scapula
humerus
ribs
vertebral column
ulna
radius
sacrum
carpals
metacarpals
phalanges
pelvic gridle
femur
patella
fibula
tibia
tarsals
metatarsals
phalanges

Figure 7.3 Skeletal System

RESPIRATORY SYSTEM

Respiration refers to the movement of air in and out of the lungs. Respiration takes place when we inhale through the process of **inspiration** (breathing in). During inspiration, air enters the nasal cavity where it passes through the trachea, bronchial tubes and alveoli (singular form alveolus). **Alveoli** are air sacs rich in blood vessels where gas exchange takes place between lungs and blood. Oxygen then diffuses into the cells and carbon dioxide moves out of the cells.

When we breathe out, we rid our bodies of carbon dioxide. Breathing out is called **expiration**. Air follows the same pathway to leave the body as it

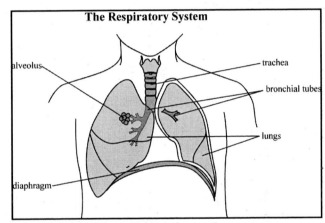

The Respiratory System

alveolus
trachea
bronchial tubes
lungs
diaphragm

Figure 7.4 Respiratory System

does to enter the body. To take a breath, a special muscle called the **diaphragm** must contract. The diaphragm is a flat muscle that runs across the body cavity below the lungs. When the diaphragm contracts, it forces air into the body. When the diaphragm relaxes, expiration occurs and air is forced out of the body.

IMMUNE SYSTEM

The immune system is a collection of cells and tissues that defend the human body against outside invaders. It consists of the **lymphatic system**, **spleen**, **tonsils**, **thymus** and **bone marrow**. Bone marrow makes **leukocytes** (white blood cells). The immune system works with your skin, respiratory system and digestive system to prevent disease.

LYMPHATIC SYSTEM

The lymphatic system is a connecting network among the parts of the immune system. It consists of **lymph vessels**, **lymph** and **lymphoid tissues** (i.e. lymph nodes, tonsils, thymus and spleen). Lymph vessels transport lymph. Lymph is the fluid contained in the lymph vessels. It is composed of tissue fluid and white blood cells. Tissue fluid is fluid surrounding cells made up of water, small molecules and leukocytes. Once tissue fluid enters the lymph vessels, it is called lymph.

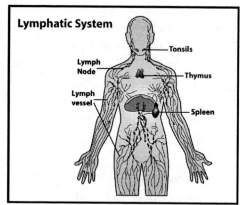

Figure 7.5 Lymphatic System

Lymph nodes filter the lymph fluid and prevent foreign particles or microorganisms from entering the bloodstream. As the lymphatic system fights these invaders, the lymph nodes can become swollen and sore.

The lymphatic system also plays a role in returning fluid to blood. The lymph vessels do not have a pump like arteries do. They operate like veins, relying on muscle contractions to push fluid throughout the body. Exercise is important to keep the lymph moving. That is why people who get regular exercise seem to be sick less often!

MUSCULAR SYSTEM

The **muscular system** is used to move the body. The muscular system works to move the body, help circulate the blood and move food through the digestive system. The three types of muscular tissue that accomplish these tasks are: skeletal, cardiac and smooth.

Skeletal muscle tissue is attached to the bones with ligaments and tendons. Skeletal muscles move the body and are a type of voluntary muscle. **Cardiac muscles** are found only in the heart and are a type of involuntary muscle. Involuntary muscle tissue contracts (or works) automatically. You don't have to think about making your heart beat, it just happens! Another type of involuntary muscle tissue is smooth muscle. **Smooth muscle** is found in many organs like the esophagus, stomach and intestines. In these ways the muscular system works with the digestive, circulatory and skeletal systems.

NERVOUS SYSTEM

The **nervous system** is the control and communication network of the body. It detects and responds to stimuli both inside and outside the body. The five senses (smell, touch, taste, sight and hearing) are controlled by this system. A **nerve** is a bundle of nerve cells, called neurons. **Neurons** carry information from one place to another.

The nervous system is broken down into two main parts: the central nervous system (CNS) and the peripheral nervous system. The **central nervous system** is composed of the brain and spinal cord. The CNS is the main control center for the human body. The **peripheral nervous system** consists of all other parts of the nervous system. The peripheral nervous system carries nerve impulses from the brain and spinal cord to the body

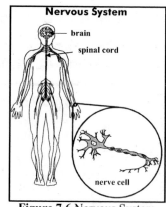

Figure 7.6 Nervous System

and carries sensory input from the body to the brain. The nerves in your fingers that detect heat are an example of the peripheral nervous system. The nervous system interacts with all the body systems in one way or another.

EXCRETORY SYSTEM

The **excretory system** removes wastes from the body. The lungs and skin release some wastes through respiration and sweating, but the majority of metabolic wastes are removed through the urinary tract. The **urinary tract** consists of the kidneys, ureters, bladder and urethra. The excretory system interacts with the respiratory, digestive, lymphatic, nervous and circulatory systems.

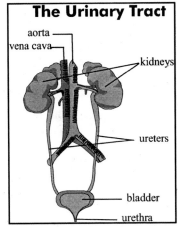

The Urinary Tract

aorta
vena cava
kidneys
ureters
bladder
urethra

Figure 7.7 Urinary Tract

REPRODUCTIVE SYSTEM

Reproduction is necessary for the continuation of a species. Human reproduction involves two parents, the male and the female. The male produces sperm cells and the female produces egg cells. Fertilization happens when the sperm and egg unite. The resulting offspring is called a zygote and further development is continued through mitosis. The reproductive system interacts with the nervous and digestive system.

Activity

To demonstrate how a lung works, we can make an artificial lung model. For this activity you will need one two-liter plastic bottle with cap, balloons, a latex glove, hot glue or Elmer's® glue (using Elmer's® glue requires longer drying time), rubber bands and a straw. Build the apparatus shown to the right.

Drill a hole in the bottle cap the same size as the straw. Insert the straw through the cap and use some glue to make it airtight. Attach a balloon to the bottom of the straw and secure with a rubber band. Cut the bottle in half and attach a balloon or latex glove with rubber bands to the bottom. Place cap on top of bottle with the balloon on the inside. Pull on the bottom of the bottle. What did you notice? What made this happen? Name the parts of the respiratory system shown in the model.

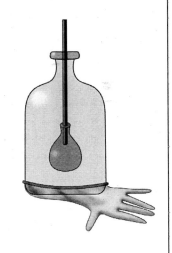

Chapter 7 Review

1. What is one major function of the lymphatic system?

   A. To transport oxygenated and deoxygenated blood.

   B. To provide support and structure for the body.

   C. To transmit information from the environment to the brain.

   D. To prevent foreign particles from entering the bloodstream.

2. How does the stomach aid in digestion?

   A. It mechanically breaks down fats.

   B. It chemically and mechanically breaks down foods.

   C. It mechanically breaks down sugars.

   D. It mechanically breaks down proteins.

3. The diaphragm contracts to

   A. force air into the lungs.

   B. force air into and out of the lungs.

   C. move the stomach to assist in the mechanical breakdown of food.

   D. support the spinal column.

4. What is the main job of the respiratory system?

   A. delivering carbon monoxide to the important parts of the body

   B. pumping blood to the capillaries

   C. taking in oxygen for respiration

   D. taking in carbon dioxide and delivering it to the cells

5. What are the main components of the circulatory system?

   A. bone marrow, ligaments and tendons

   B. heart, veins, arteries and blood

   C. brain, spinal cord and neurons

   D. stomach, esophagus and small intestine.

1. (A) (B) (C) (D)
2. (A) (B) (C) (D)
3. (A) (B) (C) (D)
4. (A) (B) (C) (D)
5. (A) (B) (C) (D)

Chapter 8
Genetics and Chromosomes

GEORGIA 7TH GRADE CRCT IN SCIENCE STANDARDS COVERED IN THIS CHAPTER INCLUDE:

S7L3a	Explain the role of genes and chromosomes in the process of inheriting a specific trait.

PARENT ORGANISM

All organisms take their structure and design from previously living organisms like themselves. The **parent organism** is the organism from which the genetic material for an offspring originated. We will learn more about asexual and sexual reproduction in the next chapter. Let's go over some basics for now:

Asexual reproduction results in offspring that are identical to the single parent. In this type of reproduction, new individuals are a product of mitosis. The parent and the offspring have identical genetic material.

Sexual reproduction is the donation of a **gamete** (a sex cell) by each parent. The resulting **zygote** (cell that results from the process of fertilization) will have characteristics of each of the contributing parents. Each new member of the species will have slightly different traits from the parents.

So, if the offspring was produced by sexual reproduction, there will be two parent organisms. Each will pass on traits to its offspring, but not all of those traits will be obvious. The passing on of traits from parent to offspring is called **heredity**. The study of traits passed from generation to generation is called **genetics**.

Hereditary characteristics are determined by specific portions of DNA called **genes**. DNA is a double stranded structure of molecules found in the chromosomes of cells which carry the information necessary to duplicate the organism. (You'll learn much more about DNA in high school!) Genes carry traits that can be passed on from one generation to the next. Alternate forms of a gene are called **alleles**. Each parent passes on one allele for each trait to the offspring. Each offspring has two alleles for each trait such as eye color.

The expression of physical characteristics depends on the genes contributed by both parents for that particular characteristic. The combination of alleles inherited from the parents is called the **genotype**. To put it another way, a person's genotype for a trait is the actual genes/alleles they carry for it, not the trait that results from those genes.

Genes are either dominant or recessive. A **dominant** gene is one that will always be expressed if it is present. If both alleles are dominant or one is dominant and one is recessive, the trait expressed will be the dominant one. If the recessive trait is to be expressed, both alleles must be the recessive ones. The physical expression of the traits is called the **phenotype**. Phenotypes do not necessarily reveal the combination of alleles present in an individual.

When studying the expression of the traits, letters are used. **Dominant** alleles are expressed in capital letters, and **recessive** alleles are expressed in lowercase letters. For instance, brown eyes are dominant to blue eyes, so a capital B is used to indicate brown eyes and a lowercase b is used for blue eyes. The genotype of the offspring having one gene for blue eyes and one gene for brown eyes is Bb. The phenotype for this example is brown eyes.

If an individual inherits two of the same alleles for a particular trait, either both dominant or both recessive, the individual is **homozygous**. If the offspring inherits one dominant allele and one recessive allele, such as in the example above, the individual is **heterozygous**. The **Punnett Square** is used to express the possible combinations for a certain trait an offspring may inherit from the parents. The Punnett Square shows possible genotypes which will determine the phenotype of an individual.

Here is an example to illustrate these concepts. A new baby is born and, as with all babies, no one can tell how tall he is going to be. All of the relatives look to the parents to solve the mystery. Here are their phenotypes: the father is taller than average, at 6' 5"; the mother is also taller than average, at 5'11". OK, so, the baby will be taller than average, right? Not necessarily. Just *looking* at someone (seeing their phenotype) does not tell us the whole story; we need to know their genotype in order to make a more informed prediction. So, let us say that genetic testing has been done (the family was *really* curious about this height thing), and it has been determined that the father and mother both have a heterozygous tall genotype. Furthermore, researchers have determined that the tall gene (T) is dominant to the short gene (t).

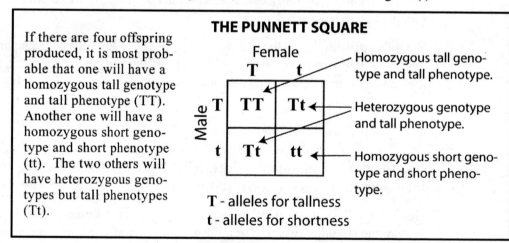

Figure 8.1

So, there is a 75% chance that the baby will end up being tall. Right? Well, sort of…

The phenotype depends not only on which genes are present, but also the environment. Environmental differences have an effect on which traits are expressed in an organism. For example, a plant seed has the genetic ability to have green tissues, to flower and to bear fruit, but it must be in the correct environmental conditions. If the required amount of light, water and nutrients are not present, those genes may not be expressed.

In essence, the baby must have good nutrition and environmental conditions in order to fulfill his genetic destiny.

There are a few situations in which genetic clarity becomes even harder to achieve. In order to describe these situations, let's name the generations. The parental generation is called the **P generation.** The offspring (the kids) of the P generation are called the **F_1 generation.** The offspring of the offspring (the grand-kids) are called the **F_2 generation.** Armed with that information, let's look at a few examples of more complicated genetic phenomena.

INCOMPLETE DOMINANCE

Incomplete dominance is the situation where one trait is not completely dominant over the other. Think of it as a blending of the two traits. This is most easily seen in plants. In this case, all of the offspring in the F_1 generation will show a phenotype that is a **blending** of both the parents. If the F_1 generation is self-pollinated, the ratio of the offspring will appear in a predictable pattern. One offspring will look like one parent, two offspring will look like both parents and one offspring will look like the other parent.

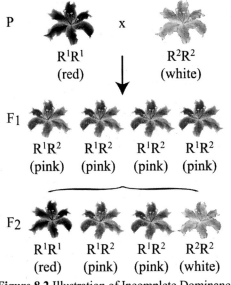

Figure 8.2 Illustration of Incomplete Dominance

A cross between a red and a white four o'clock flower demonstrates this point. One flower in the parental generation is red with genotype R^1R^1. The other flower is white with genotype R^2R^2. (Note that both genetic descriptors are in capital letters, but with different superscripts) The offspring of this cross appear pink and have a genotype of R^1R^2. See Figure 8.2 for the genotypes and the phenotypes of the P, F_1 and F_2 (first and second) generations.

CO-DOMINANCE

When both traits appear in the F_1 generation and contribute to the phenotype of the offspring, the trait is **co-dominant.** One example occurs in horses in which the trait for red hair (genotype $H^R H^R$) is co-dominant with the trait for white hair (genotype $H^W H^W$). A **roan** is a foal that has both traits (genotype $H^R H^W$). The horse appears to look pinkish-brown from far away. However, if you look closely at the coat of this animal, you will notice that both solid red and solid white hairs found on the coat give the animal its unique color. Another example of co-dominance is a calico cat with orange and black patches of color. Examine Table 8.1 to help you further understand the principle of co-dominance.

Table 8.1 Co-Dominant Expression

Genotype	Phenotype
$H^R H^R$	Red coat
$H^W H^W$	White coat
$H^R H^W$	Roan coat

Activity

Research traits on the Internet and complete different Punnett Squares for several organism characteristics. (hair color, tongue rolling, earlobe attachment, seed coat color, flower color, etc.)

Chapter 8 Review

1. The combination of alleles inherited is called the

   A. heterozygote.

   B. phenotype.

   C. genotype.

   D. Punnett square.

2. The expression of traits is called the

   A. phenotype.

   B. genotype.

   C. mutation.

   D. allele.

3. If an individual inherits one dominant allele and one recessive allele, the genotype is

   A. homozygous.

   B. recessive.

   C. heterozygous.

   D. phenotype.

4. If an individual inherits two of the same allele, either both dominant or both recessive for a particular characteristic, the individual's genotype is

   A. heterozygous.

   B. phenotypic.

   C. homozygous.

   D. mutated.

5. Use a Punnett Square to predict the cross of a homozygous green parent with a homozygous yellow parent if yellow is dominant over green. The phenotype of the offspring will be

   A. all yellow.

   B. all green.

   C. neither yellow nor green.

   D. some yellow and some green.

1. Ⓐ Ⓑ Ⓒ Ⓓ
2. Ⓐ Ⓑ Ⓒ Ⓓ
3. Ⓐ Ⓑ Ⓒ Ⓓ
4. Ⓐ Ⓑ Ⓒ Ⓓ
5. Ⓐ Ⓑ Ⓒ Ⓓ

Chapter 9
Sexual & Asexual Reproduction

GEORGIA 7TH GRADE CRCT IN SCIENCE STANDARDS COVERED IN THIS CHAPTER INCLUDE:

S7L3b	Compare and contrast sexual and asexual reproduction in organisms (bacteria, protist, fungi, plants and animals.

At this point, you know that every living thing is made of cells. How many cells are there in *your* body? Well, somewhere between 10 and 50 trillion cells are present in the average adult body, so you probably have a few less than that. Believe it or not, even at our technological best, there really is no way to know the exact number of cells in a human body right now. Can you imagine trying to count them all? To make it even harder, the number of cells in your own body is constantly changing, as cells die or are destroyed and new ones are formed. So how does the body replace cells that "wear out" and die? The answer is a replacement process called cell division.

Cell division is necessary for the normal growth, repair and reproduction of an organism. Old cells are replaced by new, fresh ones and reproductive cells are created. Some cells are replaced often, like those in the lining of the stomach. Others are seldom replaced, like those of the heart. Sometimes, cell division becomes uncontrollable and disease results. But without new cells, reproduction could not occur, genes would not be passed from one generation to the next and life would eventually cease to exist.

CELLULAR REPRODUCTION

Multicellular organisms are composed of two kinds of cells: **reproductive cells** (cells that are involved in sexual reproduction) and **somatic cells** (all other cells).

Since there are two general categories of cells, it makes sense that there are also two kinds of cell division: mitosis and meiosis. The result of mitosis is a cell identical to the one that the process began with. The result of meiosis is a reproductive cell (an egg or sperm cell), each containing only half the chromosomes a new organism needs. When they join together, they make one new cell, which then divides through mitosis and creates a new organism.

The **cell cycle** is the series of stages through which a cell passes between one cell division and the next. Most of the cell cycle is spent in **interphase**. Mitosis is a small part of the cell cycle.

Mitosis is the type of cellular reproduction used by somatic cells. Mitosis is sometimes called cell division, but it is really the division of the nucleus. Mitosis results in two cells with the same number of chromosomes.

Chromosomes carry the genetic material of the organism. Mitosis ensures that all cells are genetically identical to one another. It is also the basis of asexual reproduction of single-celled eukaryotes. **Asexual reproduction** is reproduction from only one parent. The offspring is a **clone** of the parent (genetically identical).

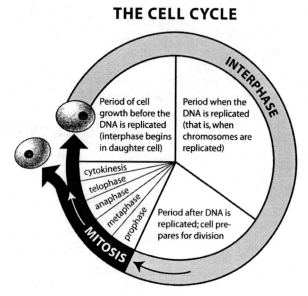

THE CELL CYCLE

Figure 9.1

Mitosis allows for unicellular organisms to reproduce asexually, and for multicellular organisms to grow and replace cells. As a cell increases in size, the need for nutrients increases, but it becomes more difficult for the cell to carry out the reactions necessary for life. To solve this problem, the cell stops growing at a certain point, and mitosis takes place, resulting in two cells of a manageable size, each able to carry out life processes more easily.

Mitosis is a vital mode of cellular reproduction in somatic cells, but reproductive cells operate differently. For sex cells (cells in the male and female that join together to form offspring) another type of cell division is needed: meiosis. **Meiosis** is limited to the reproductive cells in the testes, namely the sperm cells, and the reproductive cells in the ovaries, namely the eggs. Meiosis produces four reproductive cells, or **gametes**. These four cells contain half the number of chromosomes of the parent cell, and the chromosomes are not identical.

Meiosis is important to species reproduction because it provides genetic variation. Genetic variation gives…well, *variety* to species. It increases the species' chances of survival by giving them a greater ability to adapt to changes. It is important to note that this variation does not occur in mitosis.

SEXUAL REPRODUCTION AND EARLY GROWTH

The gametes produced during meiosis are sperm cells in men and egg cells in women. The egg cell is one of the largest cells in the human body, while the sperm cell is one of the smallest. During fertilization, the gametes fuse into a new parent cell, or **zygote**, during **fertilization**.

The zygote is the new single-celled offspring, and it can begin the process of mitosis to grow in size. Initially, all of the cells produced by mitotic division are the same. Eventually, they produce cells that are specialized and later become tissues. This process, called **cell differentiation**, is the process by which cells specialize to perform a specific function in a multicellular organism. As each cell differentiates, it produces characteristically different proteins, which distinguish it from other cell types.

Table 9.1 Comparison of Reproductive Strategies

Type of organism	Asexual reproduction	Sexual reproduction
Plants	Through vegetative propagation, spores and regeneration.	Through pollination sometimes using spores, flowers, seeds and fruits.
Animals	Through hermaphroditic animals only.	Through sex to produce offspring of the species.
Fungi	Through spores and budding.	Through spores.
Bacteria	Through binary fission or budding; similar to mitosis	Through conjugation, using a pilus
Protists	Through binary fission; similar to mitosis	Only ciliates can reproduce sexually through conjugation

Activity

Use the Internet, or library to determine the length of time it takes each cell type below to complete the cell cycle. Then identify the type of cellular division each cell uses. Use the table to help you. The first one is done for you.

skin cell, red blood cell, macrophage, hepatocyte, red skeletal muscle cell, gustatory cell, pneumocyte Type I and II, kidney cell, cardiac muscle cell, olfactory receptor neuron, neuron, melanocyte, keratinocyte and somatotropes.

Cell	Cycle time	Division type
skin cell	30 days	mitosis

Activity

Research one organism from each of the six kingdoms. Discover its lifecycle and how it reproduces. Present your findings in a table or write a short story about their lifecycles.

Chapter 9 Review

1. All body cells, except the sperm and the egg are _____ cells.

   A. germ

   B. reproductive

   C. somatic

   D. spindle

2. The type of nuclear division that produces gametes is

   A. meiosis.

   B. cytokinesis.

   C. interphase.

   D. mitosis.

3. In mitosis

   A. the result is two identical cells.

   B. the result is two cells that have half the genetic material of the parent.

   C. germ cells are produced.

   D. genetic variation occurs that is vital to species survival.

4. The length of time it takes for a cell to complete the cell cycle is

   A. around two hours.

   B. different for each cell.

   C. the same for each kind of cell.

   D. around two minutes.

5. Why is meiosis important to species?

   A. It gives species genetic variation.

   B. It creates offspring identical to the parent.

   C. It causes cell differentiation.

   D. It creates a zygote.

1. Ⓐ Ⓑ Ⓒ Ⓓ
2. Ⓐ Ⓑ Ⓒ Ⓓ
3. Ⓐ Ⓑ Ⓒ Ⓓ
4. Ⓐ Ⓑ Ⓒ Ⓓ
5. Ⓐ Ⓑ Ⓒ Ⓓ

Chapter 10
Getting Desired Traits

Copyright American Book Company. DO NOT DUPLICATE. 1-888-264-5877.

GEORGIA 7TH GRADE CRCT IN SCIENCE STANDARDS COVERED IN THIS CHAPTER INCLUDE:

S7L3c	Recognize that selective breeding can produce plants and animals with desired traits.

GETTING DESIRED TRAITS

Have you ever wondered why there are so many different kinds of tomatoes? There are large flavorful tomatoes, yellow tomatoes and tiny grape tomatoes. Many domesticated plants and animals have been changed over time because of **selective breeding**. Humans use selective breeding to pass along desired traits to future generations. In this way, humans can control many physical characteristics of an organism, from color to shape to size.

Think, for example, about horses. There are fine thoroughbreds used for racing, large bulky warmbloods used for farming and pulling carriages, hardy quick quarter horses used for ranching cattle, small riding ponies and miniature horses.

Figure 10.1 Racing Thoroughbreds

Selective breeding is achieved in the following way. If a desired trait were present in a particular horse, that horse was mated with another horse with the same characteristic. For example, to produce a miniature horse, two small individual horses would be mated to produce an even smaller offspring.

Figure 10.2 Shire Draught Horse

Sometimes selective breeding uses inbreeding to "speed up" the enhancement of a physical trait. **Inbreeding** is when two closely related animals are mated. Often inbreeding can have unforeseen consequences. Inbreeding can amplify genetic or physical weaknesses quickly in domestic animals. Inbreeding reduces **genetic diversity**.

Some would argue that domestic animals are more fragile than their wild counterparts. Thoroughbreds have been bred to have light, fine bones. This makes the horse run fast but also makes the animal more susceptible to broken bones in the leg or foot. Compare the thoroughbred to the wild American Mustang. The American Mustang is hardy, resilient and tough. Mustangs rarely suffer from broken bones, but cannot run as fast as a thoroughbred.

Sometimes selective breeding is done through the use of **hybridization**. Hybridization occurs when two genetically different parents are mated to produce a hybrid offspring. This type of selective breeding increases genetic diversity and usually produces more robust offspring. For instance, thoroughbreds are sometimes crossed with quarter horses to produce a horse called an appendix. The breeder wants the athleticism of the thoroughbred and the durability of a quarter horse.

Figure 10.3 US Long Grain Rice

Genetic engineering is also used to produce organisms with desired characteristics. Genetic engineering is the laboratory procedure in which genes from one organism are inserted into another. For example, golden rice is a genetically engineered type of rice that has bacterial DNA inserted into its own DNA. The result is a yellow-colored rice grain that is high in beta carotene.

Some selective breeding is the result of a **mutation**. Mutations are random changes in the DNA code, which cause offspring to have different characteristics than would be expected. These characteristics may be good, bad or neutral. For instance, several hundred years ago all carrots were white. The orange color found in the carrot was produced through a genetic mutation. A Dutch gardener began breeding and producing orange carrots, mostly because orange was the color of the Dutch Royal House! Orange carrots were also better because they were more nutritious then white carrots.

Figure 10.4 Carrots

CLONING

Cloning is the creation of genetically identical organisms. Cloning is accomplished through several steps. The first step is to get a donor somatic cell from an existing organism. Next, an egg cell has its nucleus removed, and the somatic cell's donor nucleus is inserted. The cloned egg cell is then stimulated to grow with electricity or hormones. The cloning of Dolly the sheep from an adult sheep cell in 1997 created great debate about the possibility of cloning humans.

The possible benefits of human cloning include allowing a childless couple to have a child, creating tissues for transplantation that would not be rejected by their host, and using genetically altered cells to treat people with Alzheimer's or Parkinson's. Both Alzheimer's and Parkinson's are caused by the death of specific cells within the brain.

Figure 10.5 Dolly and her offspring Bonnie

Although creating a human clone is theoretically possible, it would be very difficult. Dolly was the 277th attempt in cloning a mammal and her death sparked a huge array of new research questions. Both scientific and moral questions must be debated, researched and solved if cloning technology is ever to become mainstream science.

Activity

In the United States, federal research funds are not given to scientists who research human cloning, but the research is not banned. Divide into groups of 3 or 4 students and research the pros and cons of cloning. Decide if cloning research should be banned or not and put together a poster showing your point of view. Or have a class debate about banning cloning research.

Activity

Compare and contrast natural and artificial selection. Attempt to answer the question: "Do you think domesticated plants and animals could survive in the wild?"

Chapter 10 Review

1. What is inbreeding?

    A. When humans decide what traits to pass along to future generations.

    B. When two genetically different parents are mated to produce a robust offspring.

    C. When two closely related animals are mated.

    D. Random changes in the DNA.

2. What is selective breeding?

    A. When humans decide what traits to pass along to future generations.

    B. When two genetically different parents are mated to produce a robust offspring.

    C. When two closely related animals are mated.

    D. Random changes in the DNA.

3. Why is hybridization helpful to humans?

    A. It produces offspring with particular characteristics.

    B. It produces a more robust offspring.

    C. It can have unforeseen consequences.

    D. It causes random changes in the DNA.

4. Which organisms have been changed through selective breeding?

    A. horses

    B. dogs

    C. carrots

    D. all of the above

5. Which would be an example of selective breeding?

    A. A wild mustang mating with his mares.

    B. A peahen choosing to mate with the peacock that has the largest, most impressive tail.

    C. Salmon swimming upstream to spawn.

    D. Humans producing tomatoes that are large, flavorful and durable.

1. Ⓐ Ⓑ Ⓒ Ⓓ
2. Ⓐ Ⓑ Ⓒ Ⓓ
3. Ⓐ Ⓑ Ⓒ Ⓓ
4. Ⓐ Ⓑ Ⓒ Ⓓ
5. Ⓐ Ⓑ Ⓒ Ⓓ

Domain 1 Review

1. (A) (B) (C) (D)
2. (A) (B) (C) (D)
3. (A) (B) (C) (D)
4. (A) (B) (C) (D)
5. (A) (B) (C) (D)
6. (A) (B) (C) (D)
7. (A) (B) (C) (D)
8. (A) (B) (C) (D)
9. (A) (B) (C) (D)
10. (A) (B) (C) (D)

11. (A) (B) (C) (D)
12. (A) (B) (C) (D)
13. (A) (B) (C) (D)
14. (A) (B) (C) (D)
15. (A) (B) (C) (D)
16. (A) (B) (C) (D)
17. (A) (B) (C) (D)
18. (A) (B) (C) (D)
19. (A) (B) (C) (D)
20. (A) (B) (C) (D)

1. A _____ is a type of cell that has a true nucleus.

   A. prokaryote

   B. eukaryote

   C. bacterium

   D. virus

2. The necessary characteristics a substance must have in order to be classified as living are

   A. a heart and lungs.

   B. the ability to nourish itself, grow and reproduce.

   C. the ability to photosynthesize and to eliminate waste products.

   D. a true nucleus and nuclear membrane.

3. What type of energy is used to fuel the process of photosynthesis and what type is produced in respiration?

   A. Light energy is used in photosynthesis and created by respiration.

   B. ATP is used in photosynthesis, which allows the plant to undergo respiration.

   C. Light energy is used in photosynthesis, whereas respiration creates the energetic product, ATP.

   D. Food energy is used in photosynthesis and ATP is produced in respiration.

4. Two structures found in plant cells that are not found in animal cells are the

   A. mitochondria and ribosomes.

   B. cell wall and plastids.

   C. cell membrane and centrioles.

   D. nucleolus and endoplasmic reticulum.

5. Groups of cells that perform the same function are collectively known as

   A. plastids.

   B. tissues.

   C. organs.

   D. molecules.

6. Amoebas obtain food by wrapping the cell membrane around the food particle, creating a vesicle. The food is then brought into the cell. This process is called

   A. exocytosis.

   B. endocytosis.

   C. osmosis.

   D. photosynthesis.

7. Mitosis generates

   A. daughter cells identical to the mother cell.

   B. many reproductive cells.

   C. diseased cells.

   D. gametes.

8. Meiosis is a type of cell division that

   A. leads to genetic mutation.

   B. creates somatic cells.

   C. is necessary for sexual reproduction.

   D. causes alleles to deform.

9. A type of cellular reproduction when the nuclear division of somatic cells takes place is

   A. meiosis.

   B. cytokinesis.

   C. interphase.

   D. mitosis.

10. Somatic cells reproduce using

A. sexual reproduction.

B. asexual reproduction.

C. gametes.

D. mutations.

11. The F_1 generation of snapdragon plants reveals a distinct blending of phenotype. What is the reason for this?

A. The two plants crossed in the P generation had alleles that were incompletely dominant to each other.

B. The two plants crossed in the P generation had alleles that were co-dominant to each other.

C. The P generation consisted of only heterozygous genotypes.

D. The F_1 generation consisted of only homozygous genotypes.

12. DNA is located primarily in

A. the cell wall.

B. the cytoplasm.

C. the nucleus.

D. the ribosome.

13. The smooth muscle tissue contracts to

A. force air into and out of the lungs.

B. force air into and out of the stomach.

C. move the stomach to assist in the mechanical breakdown of food.

D. support the spinal column.

Use the following Punnett Square to answer questions 14 and 15.

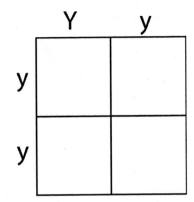

14. What is the probability that the offspring of this cross will be homozygous recessive?

A. 0%

B. 25%

C. 50%

D. 100%

15. What is the probability that the offspring of this cross will be homozygous dominant?

A. 0%

B. 25%

C. 50%

D. 100%

16. What is the function of the lymphatic system?

A. causing swelling in capillaries

B. pumping blood to the capillaries

C. taking in oxygen for energy

D. fighting infection

17. The P generation of orchid flowers includes one red flower and one white flower. Crossing the two results in flowers with red and white patches of color. This is an example of

   A. incomplete dominance.

   B. co-dominance.

   C. multiple alleles.

   D. a polygenic trait.

18. Which of the following questions would be useful when developing a dichotomous key about the cats seen here?

African Leopard   African Lion

   A. Does the cat have fur?

   B. Does the cat have spots?

   C. Does the cat have four paws?

   D. Does the cat live in Africa?

19. Which of the following lists the current six kingdoms?

   A. kingdom, phylum, class, order, family, genus and species

   B. plantae, animalia, fungi, protista, archae-bacteria and eubacteria

   C. plants, animals, fungus, bacteria and dia-toms

   D. animalia, chordata, mammalia, primates, hominidae, *Homo* and *H. sapiens*

20. Which selective breeding technique would be used to produce a white-colored dog?

   A. Use a laboratory procedure to insert white mice genes into a dog fetus.

   B. Breed a light-colored dog with a dark colored dog.

   C. Breed two dark-colored dogs.

   D. Breed two light-colored dogs.

Domain 2
Interdependence of Life

Chapter 11: Food Webs Matter   S7L4a

In this chapter, topics discussed include food chains, food webs and common ecological terminology.

Chapter 12: Transfer of Energy   S7L4b

This chapter focuses on energy pyramids, trophic levels and sources of energy for organisms.

Chapter 13: Environment and Organisms   S7L4c

This chapter covers the characteristics of populations such as growth rate, density, carrying capacity, limiting factors and the effects of environmental change on populations.

Chapter 14: Organism Relationships   S7L4d

This chapter introduces students to associations between organisms. Topics such as mutualism, commensalism, parasitism, competition and predation are covered. Students are given examples of each kind of relationship.

Chapter 15: Earth's Biomes   S7L4e

In this chapter, topics discussed include the main biomes found on Earth and common ecological terminology. Biomes covered include tundra, coniferous forest, deciduous forest, grassland, tropical rain forest, desert, freshwater ecosystems and marine ecosystems.

Make a Concept Map

Use the blank space here to develop your own concept map about topics in Domain 2. Complete this activity **before** beginning the domain to find out what you may already know about ecology! Then at the end of the domain return to your concept map and add or change things you learned in this section. Use **Appendix A** to help you build your map.

Chapter 11
Food Webs Matter

S7L4a	Demonstrate in a food web that matter is transferred from one organism to another and can recycle between organisms and their environments.

INTERACTION AND INTERDEPENDENCE

Matter within an ecosystem is constantly recycled over and over again. Elements, chemical compounds and other sources of matter pass from one state to another through the ecosystem, so that the amount of these substances remains consistent on Earth. As a deer eats grass, the nutrients contained in the grass are broken down into their chemical components and then rearranged to become living deer tissue. Waste products are produced in the deer's digestive system and pass from the deer's body back into the ecosystem. Organisms break down this waste into simpler chemical components. The grass growing close by is able to take up those components and utilize them; they become a part of the grass. Then, the cycle begins again.

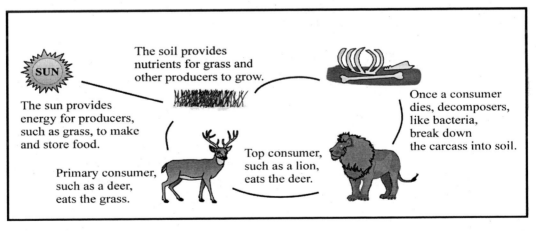

Figure 11.1 Energy Cycle

FOOD CHAINS AND FOOD WEBS

The producers, consumers and decomposers of each ecosystem make up a **food chain**. Energy flow through an ecosystem occurs in food chains, with energy passing from one organism to another. There can be many food chains in an ecosystem.

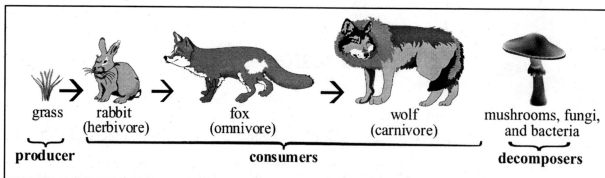

grass | rabbit (herbivore) | fox (omnivore) | wolf (carnivore) | mushrooms, fungi, and bacteria

producer | **consumers** | **decomposers**

Figure 11.2 A Food Chain

The **producers** of an ecosystem use **abiotic** (not living) factors to obtain and store energy for themselves or the consumers that eat them. In a forest ecosystem (like much of Georgia), the producers are *trees, bushes, shrubs, small plants, grass* and *moss*.

The **consumers** are members of the ecosystem that depend on other members for food. Each time a plant or animal consumes another organism, energy transfers to the consumer. *Deer, foxes, rabbits, raccoons, owls, hawks, snakes, mice, spiders* and *insects* are examples of consumers in a forest ecosystem. There are three types of consumers: **herbivores**, **carnivores** and **omnivores**. The table below lists characteristics of the three different types of consumers.

Table 11.1 What Different Consumers Eat

Consumer	Food Supply
Herbivore	animals that eat only plants
Omnivore	animals that eat both plants and other animals
Carnivore	animals that eat only other animals
Saprophyte	organisms that obtain food from dead organisms or from the waste products of living organisms

The **decomposers** are members of the ecosystem that use dead or decaying organisms as a source of energy. As they feed on this organic matter, they further reduce it to its simplest chemical components. Decomposers include fungi and bacteria. They are also called **saprophytes**.

The interaction of many food chains is a **food web**. Most producers and consumers interact with many others, forming a complex food web out of several simple food chains. The image below shows the more complex food web.

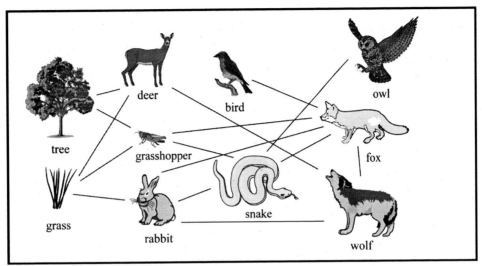

Figure 11.3 A Food Web

When you think of a predator, do you think of a lion? Or a shark? How about a big, scary…woodpecker? Well, a **predator** is any organism that feeds on other living things, typically animals, but also insects and plants. The organism it feeds on is the **prey**. So, woodpeckers qualify as predators; their prey are the insects they remove from tree trunks.

Predator and prey together help maintain an **ecological balance** within their ecosystem. This balance benefits the community as a whole, but can be either helpful or harmful to the individuals that make up the community, depending upon whether they are the predator or the prey.

Activity

Arrange the classroom chairs in a circle. This activity is best done with ten or more students. Toss a ball of yarn around the circle from one student to the next. Each student should hold one or several points of the yarn. Eventually the yarn will resemble a web. Pretend one student goes extinct, that student should drop their point of yarn. Observe the effect on the food web. What was the overall effect of the extinction of one species? Now pretend several students go extinct. What was the overall effect on the food web? This activity can be taken a step further by each student pretending to be a particular organism in the food web. The yarn should then only lead to the organism's prey or predators.

Activity

Research a particular ecosystem or biome (i.e. desert, rainforest or grassland). List all the organisms found in this environment. Arrange a food web using all the organisms. Use magazines, drawings or the Internet to make a poster showing your food web.

Chapter 11 Review

1. The owl is a nocturnal hunter of small mammals, insects and other birds. An owl is an example of a/an

   A. producer.

   B. omnivore.

   C. carnivore.

   D. decomposer.

2. Animals that eat both plants and other animals are

   A. herbivores.

   B. carnivores.

   C. omnivores.

   D. decomposers.

3. The interactions of many food chains is a(n)

   A. food web.

   B. trophic level.

   C. abiotic factor.

   D. ecological balance.

4. In a deciduous forest hundreds of dead leaves fall to the forest floor each autumn. Which group of organisms breaks down this tissue for food?

   A. herbivore

   B. omnivore

   C. carnivore

   D. saprophyte

5. Which of the following organisms is an omnivore?

   A. lion

   B. squirrel

   C. flower

   D. bear

1. Ⓐ Ⓑ Ⓒ Ⓓ
2. Ⓐ Ⓑ Ⓒ Ⓓ
3. Ⓐ Ⓑ Ⓒ Ⓓ
4. Ⓐ Ⓑ Ⓒ Ⓓ
5. Ⓐ Ⓑ Ⓒ Ⓓ

Chapter 12
Transfer of Energy

S7L4b	Explain in a food web that sunlight is a source of energy and that this energy moves from organism to organism.

Ecosystems include living and nonliving factors, and humans are a key component. That means that *you* are a part of the ecosystem in which you live. Through our interaction with these biotic and abiotic factors, we help sustain ecosystems and they, in turn, help sustain us.

ENERGY FLOW

Let's "twist the kaleidoscope" a bit and look at your ecosystem from a participant's point of view. What is provided for you? What do you provide? One answer to both questions is energy.

The fuel that gives your human body (considered to be a part of the animal kingdom) energy comes from the plants and animals you consume. This living material is called **biotic matter**. If there were no mechanism to recycle this matter (and the energy it contains), eventually the ecosystem would break down and all those within it (including you) would perish. Before you become too worried about it, relax: biotic matter and the energy contained in it *is* recycled through the ecosystem (including you). Here is how it works.

Elements, chemical compounds and other sources of matter pass from one state to another through the ecosystems. Remember the cycle outlined in the previous chapter: producer to primary consumer to secondary consumer to decomposer. Where do you fit in? Are you a producer? Well, in ecological terms, you are a consumer; in fact, humans are called **top consumers**. That means that we essentially have no competition for resources. We eat all manner of animals and plants, which we then digest and excrete. It may be unpleasant to think about, but humans do take energy out of ecosystems by consuming biotic matter and do put energy back into it through waste products and, ultimately, through decomposition. In other words, we humans do our part in taking and giving energy.

TROPHIC LEVELS

When one organism is consumed by another, its energy transfers as a part of the digestive process. However, not all organisms give the same amount of energy. Take a look at the **energy pyramid** on the right. If you carefully examine it, you should see that the amount of energy decreases as organisms go up the food chain. A **trophic level** is the position occupied by an organism in a food chain. Organisms that

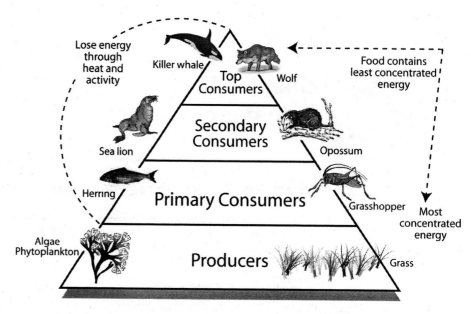

Figure 12.1 Energy Pyramid

share a trophic level get their energy from the same sources. Let's put our producers, consumers and decomposers into the energy pyramid, as in Figure 12.1.

Plants are found at the base of the energy pyramid and comprise the *first* trophic level of the food chain. They are called **producers**. Why? They "produce" their own energy by making their own food (natural sugars, remember *photosynthesis*?). The energy that drives the food making process (photosynthesis) comes from the Sun. Above producers are the **primary consumers** — they make up the *second* trophic level. These are the organisms that eat plants. Sometimes you are a **primary consumer**…when you eat your fruits and vegetables. Above the primary consumers are the **secondary consumers**, which occupy the *third* trophic level. These are organisms that eat the primary consumers. Finally, there are the **tertiary consumers** at the *top* trophic level.

The greatest *concentration* of energy exists at the base of the pyramid, with plants. Herbivores, like the grasshopper and herring, are getting a highly concentrated source of energy when they consume their food. The energy from the food is used up fairly quickly, though. What happens to that energy once the grasshopper uses it? Is it gone or destroyed? Absolutely not! Energy is not destroyed, it simply changes form. The nutrients that comprise the leaves become a part of the grasshopper, giving it fuel and allowing it to grow, to repair itself and to reproduce. Essentially, the plant energy is used to drive physical processes and is dispersed as heat.

Let's take this to the next step: the grasshopper gets attacked by a hungry opossum and is killed. The opossum eats the grasshopper. Bad for the grasshopper; good for the opossum. But how good? What about the energy? Does the opossum get as much energy from the grasshopper as the grasshopper did from its lunch? Of course it does — *it just gets it less efficiently.*

This is a very important concept. You may have wondered how a huge animal like an elephant or a whale or, for that matter, a brontosaurus, can grow to such a huge size by eating plant matter. It is because plant matter is a concentrated nutritional powerhouse. A grasshopper is a much less concentrated source of nutrition. Pound for pound, you have to eat more grasshopper to get the same nutrients contained in the grass the grasshopper had for lunch. Now, just think how far removed that fast-food hamburger and its accompanying fries are from nutritious. Think hard. Seriously, go get an apple instead.

Activity

Make your own energy pyramid using animals from familiar ecosystems. Use the image below to help you.

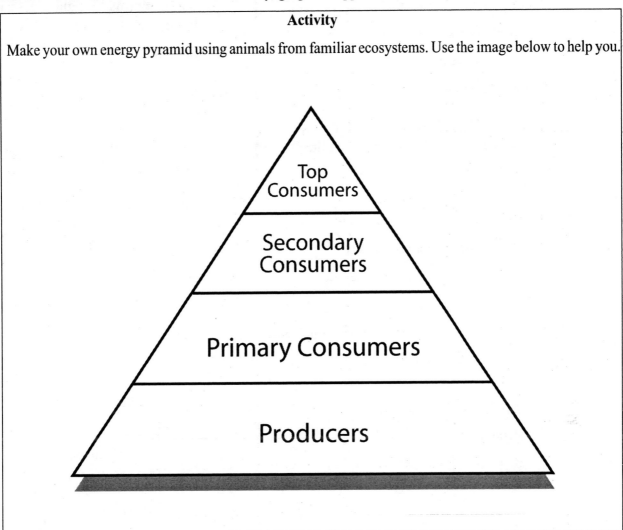

Activity

Write down everything you eat in one day. Next, trace the source of energy of everything on your list.

Chapter 12 Review

1. Organisms that share a trophic level are

   A. elephants and lions.

   B. cheetahs and giraffes.

   C. chipmunks and squirrels.

   D. wolves and sparrows.

2. In what way do the organisms of the upper trophic levels have less energy than the organisms of the lower trophic levels?

   A. Their food has less energy.

   B. Their food has less concentrated energy.

   C. Their bodies have less energy.

   D. Their bodies have less concentrated energy.

3. The bottom of the energy pyramid is made up of which kind of organisms?

   A. producers

   B. primary consumers

   C. secondary consumers

   D. top consumers

4. Why is sunlight important to ecosystems?

   A. Sunlight provides light necessary for living things to see.

   B. Sunlight provides all energy needed by living things.

   C. Sunlight is the only source of heat needed by living things.

   D. Sunlight provides the energy needed for producers to make food.

5. Which animal below is only a primary consumer?

   A. fox

   B. grass

   C. horse

   D. wolf

1. (A) (B) (C) (D)
2. (A) (B) (C) (D)
3. (A) (B) (C) (D)
4. (A) (B) (C) (D)
5. (A) (B) (C) (D)

Chapter 13
Environment and Organisms

GEORGIA 7TH GRADE CRCT IN SCIENCE STANDARDS COVERED IN THIS CHAPTER INCLUDE:

S7L4c	Recognize that changes in environmental conditions can affect the survival of both individuals and entire species.

POPULATION DYNAMICS

To refresh your memory, a **population** is a group of organisms of the same species living in the same geographic area. In your case you might call the group of people living in your city, subdivision or apartment complex a population. Important characteristics of populations include the **growth rate** (how much the population as a whole grows, rather than its individuals) and **density** (how many organisms per unit of space). The study of these characteristics is called **population dynamics**.

GROWTH

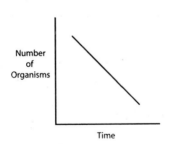

Figure 13.1 Graph of Negative Growth Rate

The **growth rate** of a population is its change in population size per unit of time. In other words, how many additional organisms have become a part of the population, over a given period of time. Organisms can enter the population through birth or **immigration** (organisms moving *into* a population). Organisms can leave the population by death or **emigration** (organisms moving *out of* a population). If a population has more births than deaths and immigration and emigration amounts are equal, then the population will grow. Ecologists observe the growth rate of a population over a number of hours, years or decades. It can be zero, positive (more in the population than before) or negative (fewer in the population than before). Think of your city. The population of cities depends on move-ins, move-outs, births and deaths. Cities can grow if more people move into them than leave, or they can shrink if more people leave than arrive. When as many people emigrate as those who immigrate, birth and death rates determine the degree of population growth — zero, negative or positive.

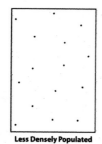

Figure 13.2 Population Density

The **density** of a population is the number of organisms per unit area; the more organisms living in a given amount of space, the denser the population in that space. Let's look at a practical example. The state of Georgia is ranked 9th in population and 24th in land area. By comparison, the state of New Jersey is ranked 10th in population and 47th in land area. Which state has a greater population density? By the ranking, you can infer that the state of New Jersey has about the same amount of people living in a smaller area than does the state of Georgia. That means that Georgia has a lower population density than New Jersey does.

CARRYING CAPACITY

The **carrying capacity** is the number of individuals that a given environment can support. A thriving population with plenty of resources expands — meaning that more offspring are born and that each organism lives longer. Eventually, the population expands beyond its carrying capacity. At that point, there is a natural downturn. As the population uses up resources, more effort has to be put into obtaining them and competition for resources increases. Population growth slows, as fewer offspring are born and organisms die younger. This downturn reduces the population back to its carrying capacity. But what determines the carrying capacity of a given population?

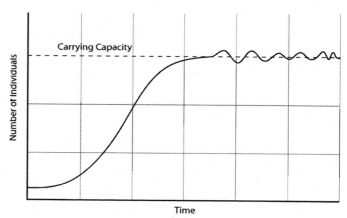

Figure 13.3 Carrying Capacity

POPULATION SIZE AND LIMITING FACTORS

In the wild and your city, population cannot continue to grow exponentially without reaching some environmental limits, such as lack of nutrients, energy, disease, living space and other resources. These are called **limiting factors** because they limit how many members of a population can be sustained in an area. There are two main categories of limiting factors: **density-dependent factors** and **density-independent factors**.

DENSITY DEPENDENT FACTORS

Density-dependent factors are issues like *competition, disease* and *predation* that only become limiting when a population in a given area reaches a certain size. Density-dependent factors usually only affect large, dense populations and rarely affect small, sparse populations. In humans, disease is often the most visible limiting factor. When a city grows too fast or has a huge population increase, adequate health care may be difficult to obtain, and so the death rate increases.

Figure 13.4 Example of Density-dependent Factor

DENSITY INDEPENDENT FACTOR

Density independent factors affect all individuals within an area, regardless of population size or density. Density-independent factors include unusual weather, natural disasters and seasonal cycles. Human modifications to the environment — like damming a river — also have broad ecological effects that are density-independent.

Figure 13.5 Tornado

CHANGED ENVIRONMENTAL CONDITIONS

When conditions change, some species (as luck would have it) already have adaptations, or characteristics, that allow them to survive and reproduce, while others do not. If the environment changes slowly enough, it's possible that a species will be able to make the necessary adaptations over many generations. This happens when the individuals in the population that have the advantageous characteristics reproduce and thrive, while those lacking these characteristics do not.

If conditions change faster than a species can adapt, the species will most likely become extinct. Sometimes, though, species are able to adapt even when an environmental change is sudden. For example, you may have heard about bacteria that have become resistant to certain antibiotics in the last few years. This resistance on the part of the bacteria toward the antibiotics is the result of a few bacteria that were naturally resistant to a specific antibiotic surviving and reproducing. In many ways, this is a numbers game. The more individuals of a species there are, the greater the mathematical possibility that individual organisms exist that are better suited to a suddenly changed environment, and the higher the likelihood that they will reproduce and eventually replenish the population. Also, the faster the reproductive cycle of the species, the more quickly the adaptation will become a dominant characteristic in the population.

Activity

Use the data below along with graph paper to make five graphs of the populations below. Then determine if each population has a positive, negative or zero growth rate. Finally, group your graphs together according to growth rate and secure on poster board.

Honey Bees		Brazilian Nut Trees		Mosquitoes in Bog	
Week 1	509	1800	95	Spring	182
Week 2	653	1850	52	Summer	563
Week 3	945	1900	43	Autumn	262
Week 4	1397	1950	38	Winter	83
Week 5	1538	Today	22	Spring	196

Alaskan King crab		Bacterial Cells	
October	2,655	Hour 1	5
November	2,013	Hour 2	56
December	1,321	Hour 3	594
January	860	Hour 4	2,637
February	533	Hour 5	10,362

Chapter 13 Review

1. What is the density of a population?

   A. How much matter is packed into a space.

   B. The number of organisms per unit area.

   C. The change in a population of organisms per unit time.

   D. The limit to how many members of a population can live in a certain area.

2. What are some things that can limit a population?

   A. nutrients

   B. space

   C. disease

   D. all of the above

3. Too many deer live in a state park. The deer are dying from starvation. What kind of limiting factor is this an example of?

   A. density-dependent

   B. density-independent

   C. carrying capacity

   D. disease

4. What are two ways a population can shrink?

   A. births and immigration

   B. deaths and emigration

   C. births and emigration

   D. deaths and immigration

5. If an environment changes slowly over time, what will most likely happen to species living in that environment?

   A. The species will remain unchanged and continue to thrive.

   B. The species will change over many generations to suit the new environment.

   C. The species will become extinct.

   D. Individuals within the population will suddenly grow new physical adaptations.

1. Ⓐ Ⓑ Ⓒ Ⓓ
2. Ⓐ Ⓑ Ⓒ Ⓓ
3. Ⓐ Ⓑ Ⓒ Ⓓ
4. Ⓐ Ⓑ Ⓒ Ⓓ
5. Ⓐ Ⓑ Ⓒ Ⓓ

Chapter 14
Organism Relationships

GEORGIA 7TH GRADE CRCT IN SCIENCE STANDARDS COVERED IN THIS CHAPTER INCLUDE:

S7L4d	Categorize relationships between organisms that are competitive or mutually beneficial.

RELATIONSHIPS BETWEEN ORGANISMS

Each organism in an ecosystem interrelates with the other members. These relationships fall into one of three categories: **symbiosis**, **competition** or **predation**.

SYMBIOSIS

A **symbiotic relationship** is a long-term association between two members of a community in which one or both parties benefit. There are three types of symbiotic relationship: **commensalism, mutualism** and **parasitism**.

Mutualism is a symbiotic relationship that is beneficial to both organisms. Protozoa living in termite intestines are an example of mutualism. The protozoa break down wood the termite eats, while the termite provides food and shelter for the protozoa. The protozoa are dependent on their termite host, and the termite is dependent on the protozoa. Both organisms benefit from each other.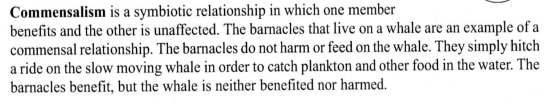

Commensalism is a symbiotic relationship in which one member benefits and the other is unaffected. The barnacles that live on a whale are an example of a commensal relationship. The barnacles do not harm or feed on the whale. They simply hitch a ride on the slow moving whale in order to catch plankton and other food in the water. The barnacles benefit, but the whale is neither benefited nor harmed.

Parasitism is a symbiotic relationship that benefits one organism (the parasite), but harms the other (the host). For example, tapeworms in a human are parasites. The tapeworm benefits by getting its nutrition from the intestines of its human host. The host, however, is harmed, because there are not as many nutrients to absorb into its body.

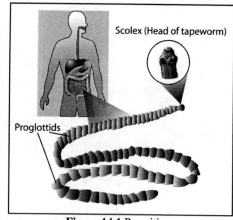

Figure 14.1 Parasitism

COMPETITION

When two or more organisms seek the same limited **resource,** they **compete** with each other. A **resource** could be food, water, light, ground space or nesting space. Competition can be intraspecific or interspecific. **Intraspecies competition** occurs between members of the same species, whereas **interspecies competition** occurs between members of different species.

PREDATION

Recall that a predator is an organism that feeds off of another organism; the prey is the organism it feeds on. It is worth saying again, that the interdependence of predator and prey has a pivotal effect on an ecosystem. Think of the scenario illustrated way back in Figure 12.1: sea lions hunt down and kill herring. They harry the edges of the school until they have killed all of the weak (old or young) and sick animals. Does that sound opportunistic and cruel to you? Maybe so, but without predation, competition and disease, there would be no natural limitations on population growth. To put it another way, it may seem brutal that organisms feed off of one another and awful that organisms perish from losing the competition for resources or disease, but the alternative is even more disastrous — an ever-more-crowded world in which every population increases until there is no space or food left for anything or anyone. With that in mind, it should be evident that ecological balances are very important indeed.

Predator/prey relationships can be represented using a graph as in Figure 14.2. Notice how the predator population mimics the prey population.

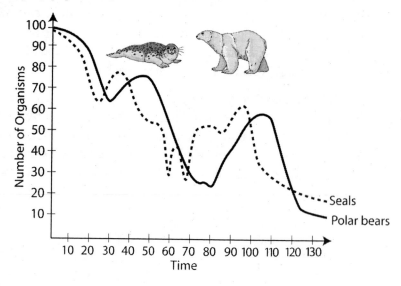

Figure 14.2 Predator/Prey Relationship

Activity

Use the organism descriptions below to classify each relationship. Relationships between organisms can be competitive, predator/prey, parasitic, mutualistic or commensalistic.

- Remoras attach themselves to sharks with a special suction cup on their heads. Remoras clean the shark's skin and eat scraps of food created when the shark feeds.

- Heartworm is a type of roundworm that enters the bloodstream of the dog from a mosquito bite. The heartworm clogs the vessels and chambers of the heart, eventually killing the dog.

- The hawk searches for and captures mice. The hawk kills and consumes the mouse.

- Pine trees and deciduous trees both need sunlight to survive. Both pine trees and deciduous trees live in the same environment.

- The cuckoo bird lays its egg in the warbler's nest. The cuckoo baby is raised by the warbler and the warbler's offspring perish.

- The butterfly feeds on nectar produced by the flower. The flower uses the pollen transported by the butterfly for reproduction.

- Both the spider and the praying mantis hunt and kill other small invertebrates. The spider and the praying mantis live in the same environment.

- Legumes have nitrifying bacteria that grow on their root systems. The bacteria convert atmospheric nitrogen to a form easily used by the legumes. The legumes are helped and the bacteria are unaffected.

- The spotted cleaner shrimp lives in a sea anemone. The shrimp cleans dead cells and parasites from the anemone and the anemone protects the shrimp from predators.

- Crows in Japan use the moving automobiles of humans to crack nuts. The crows drop the nuts in traffic and after a car runs over the nut, the crow flies down to eat the nut. Humans are unaffected by this behavior.

- A deer consumes grass, trees and shrubs.

Activity

Collect pictures from magazines, newspapers or the Internet of the plants and animals in the above list. Then group together the plants and animals with their correct relationship to make a poster.

Chapter 14 Review

1. In the rainforest, strangler figs (*Ficus citrifolia*) are a vine that grow on top of existing trees. In time, the fig vine kills the existing tree. What type of relationship is this?

   A. mutualism

   B. commensalism

   C. parasitism

   D. predator/prey

2. A tick on a dog is an example of a _____ relationship

   A. mutualistic

   B. commensalistic

   C. parasitic

   D. predator/prey

3. In which kind of relationship do both species benefit?

   A. mutualism

   B. commensalism

   C. parasitism

   D. predator/prey

4. How does predation help prey populations?

   A. Predation naturally limits populations by preventing overcrowding and starvation.

   B. Predation does not help prey populations and is a form of parasitism.

   C. Predation encourages mutualistic relationships to develop.

   D. Predation artificially limits populations and only prevents overcrowding.

5. Hermit crabs live in shells that were abandoned by snails. This neither helps nor harms the snails. What type of relationship is this?

   A. mutualism

   B. commensalism

   C. parasitism

   D. predator/prey

1. Ⓐ Ⓑ Ⓒ Ⓓ
2. Ⓐ Ⓑ Ⓒ Ⓓ
3. Ⓐ Ⓑ Ⓒ Ⓓ
4. Ⓐ Ⓑ Ⓒ Ⓓ
5. Ⓐ Ⓑ Ⓒ Ⓓ

Chapter 15
Earth's Biomes

GEORGIA 7TH GRADE CRCT IN SCIENCE STANDARDS COVERED IN THIS CHAPTER INCLUDE:

S7L4e	Describe the characteristics of Earth's major terrestrial biomes (i.e., tropical rain forest, savannah, temperate, desert, taiga, tundra and mountain) and aquatic communities (i.e., freshwater, estuaries and marine).

THE BIOSPHERE

Let's think of living things on the Earth in terms of a wide-screen epic movie. In the opening scene the camera is on the widest angle possible and you see shots of the entire Earth from space. At that point, you'd be looking at the **biosphere**, which is the thin zone around the outside of the Earth that contains all living things. The biosphere contains self-sustaining ecosystems (we'll learn more about ecosystems later) composed of biotic and abiotic factors. Recall that biotic factors include all living things, such as birds, insects, trees and flowers. **Abiotic** factors are those components of the ecosystem that are not living, but are integral in determining the number and types of organisms that are present. Examples of abiotic factors include soil, water, temperature and amount of light. In order

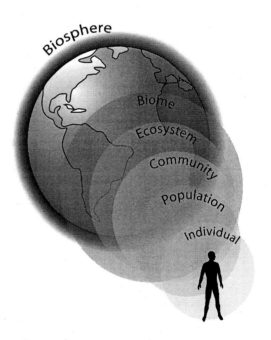

Figure 15.1 Divisions of the Biosphere

for an ecosystem to succeed, its biotic factors must obtain and store energy. In addition, the biotic and abiotic factors of the ecosystem must recycle water, oxygen, carbon and nitrogen.

For the second scene, you see the camera zoom in and focus on specific regions of the Earth that have unique climate demands for living things. Each unique climate is characterized by a dominant form of plant life. This set of shots is looking at the Earth's **biomes**. The shots in this scene will include shots of *tundras, temperate forests, islands, deserts, tropical dry forests, cold climate forests, grasslands, savannahs and tropical rainforests.*

The third scene shows how plants, animals and other organisms relate to one another and how both relate and interact with the environment in which they live. At this point you are looking at **ecosystems**. An ecosystem can be as large as a desert, or as small as a puddle. Ecosystems can be a difficult concept to grasp because it is a **system**. It's NOT the animals, plants, microorganisms or any element of the environment alone; it is the way they all relate to each other that forms the complete package of an ecosystem. Think of it like a puzzle where you can only see the full picture when the puzzle has all the pieces.

The fourth scene shows a smaller area within the ecosystem where certain types of plants or animals live in close proximity to each other. These are shots of **communities**. Examples of communities include a *densely wooded area, a clearing in a forest* or *an area near the edge of a clearing.* A community might have very different types of plants and animals living in one area — that is, the community is divided into **populations** of individual **species**. (Recall from Chapter 2 that a species is a group of similar organisms that can breed with one another to produce fertile offspring) The members of a community — various species — must interrelate with each other. Deer grazing in a clearing in the

Figure 15.2 A Community

forest may be alert to the activity or movement of birds that warn them of approaching danger. In turn, the population of birds may come to depend on the deer grazing in a clearing to disturb and flush insects hiding in the grass.

For our fifth scene we zoom in even further and begin to see things from individual plant and animal points of view. We see where the plants and animals live and eat. We look at individual community members' **habitats**. A woodpecker lives in a hole in a tree. It eats the insects that live in the bark of the tree. A robin builds its nest and raises its young in the same tree. A mouse lives in a burrow at the base of the tree. An owl sleeps on a branch of the same tree. The tree supports whole populations of organisms and becomes their habitat. The habitat provides food and shelter for the members of the community. In turn, each species of the tree community has its own **niche**, or place, as a member of the community.

A CLOSER LOOK

So far we have only five scenes in our movie, which is hardly enough to cover the price of admission! Let's go a bit deeper into detail so our audience sees a variety of settings and locations. This may not sound ultra-exciting, but if we are going to make this video an accurate representation of living things on Earth we have to start with…*plants.* Plants make most of the ecological foundation for ecosystems. Because plants are generally stationary organisms, they cannot respond to rapidly changing environmental conditions. If the amount of rainfall or sunlight received in an area did not happen in a predictably cyclic way, most plant species would become extinct. The general climate found in an area determines the plant species that will grow under those conditions. A hot, humid and rainy climate will be favorable to jungle-like plants. The plant types found in an area will determine the animal species that live there. There are six major terrestrial ecological systems (called biomes) and three major aquatic ecological systems. We'll take a closer look at each of them in the next few sections.

BIOMES

Biomes are large land area ecosystems characterized by a dominant form of plant life and climate type. Organisms living in biomes have adapted to the climate of the geographic region. There are no actual lines to indicate where one biome ends and another begins; instead, one area gradually merges into the next. Also, as climate changes occur, the general area of a biome will shift.

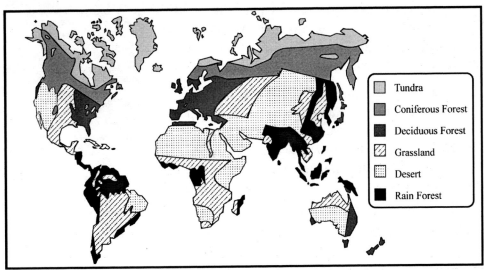

Tundra
Coniferous Forest
Deciduous Forest
Grassland
Desert
Rain Forest

Figure 15.3 Biomes of the Earth

TERRESTRIAL ECOSYSTEMS

The **tundra** biome is located near the north and south poles. Rainfall is light and summer temperatures average only 1° C (34°F). The land in the tundra has gently rolling plains with subsoil that is permanently frozen. There are many lakes, ponds and bogs. Grasses are present, but only a very few small trees grow here and there. The small plants mostly consist of *mosses, lichens and reindeer moss*. Examples of animals found in tundra areas are *reindeer, caribou, polar bears, arctic wolves, foxes, hares, lemmings, birds and insects*.

Figure 15.4 Tundra

Figure 15.5 Deciduous Forest

The **coniferous forest** biome is found above 60°N latitude. Rainfall is medium and the average summer temperature is around 12°C (54°F). In the coniferous forest, the subsoil thaws for a few weeks in summer. The land is dotted with lakes, ponds and bogs. The trees are mostly coniferous, such as *spruce and fir*. There are only a few deciduous trees, which shed or lose their leaves at the end of the growing season. Examples of animals living in coniferous forest areas are *moose, black bears, wolves, lynx, wolverines, martens, porcupines and birds*.

The **deciduous forest** biome is found in the middle latitudes, between 20° and 60°N latitude. Georgia falls into this biome, as you can see in Figure 15.3. The deciduous forest has variations in rainfall, but in general, the rainfall is moderate. The average summer temperature is around 24°C (75°F). The deciduous forest has trees, broadleaf with foliage that changes color in autumn. Trees ofter found in this biome include *maples, oaks, elms, dogwoods and beech*. The animals consist mostly of *squirrels, deer, foxes and bears*.

The **grassland** biome is located in the mid-continental areas of middle latitude. This biome is found in regions that have warm and cold cycles as well as in the tropic regions on the savannas with wet and dry cycles. In general, the rainfall is low, and the average summer temperature is 20°C (68°F). There are large **herbivores** on the savannas such as *bison, pronghorn antelope and zebras.* as well as smaller herbivores such as *burrowing rodents and prairie dogs.*

Figure 15.6 Grassland Biome

The **tropical rain forest** biome is found near the equator and near mountain ranges. Rainfall is abundant and the air is very humid. The average summer temperature is 25°C (77°F). Trees are very tall with dense canopies. The floor of the tropical rain forest does not get much sunlight, but it does keep a fairly constant temperature. There is a great diversity of species of both plants and animals including *strangler figs, nut trees, fruit trees, primates, orchids, sloths and many insects.*

The **desert** biome is found on either side of the equator between 0° and 20° latitudes. This biome gets little rain and has extreme temperature fluctuations. The average summer temperature is 30°C (86°F). There is not much grass in the desert, but what is there is very drought resistant. Other plants, like *sagebrush, mesquite and cacti*, have also adapted to desert conditions. Animals common to the desert are the *kangaroo rat, snakes, lizards, some birds, spiders and insects.*

AQUATIC ECOSYSTEMS

On land, temperature and precipitation are very important in determining what kind of life can be supported. In the water, the determining factors are very different. These factors include: amount of light, oxygen and the **salinity** (salt) level of the water. The amount of salt in the water is the most important factor in determining the type of organisms in the ecosystem. Light and oxygen are important for photosynthesis. Aquatic ecosystems include *marine areas, freshwater areas* and *estuaries,* all of which are determined by the salinity of the area.

Freshwater ecosystems consist of streams, rivers, lakes, marshes and swamps. Freshwater areas have a low salt content, or low salinity. They are found in most places on Earth. Fresh water is important in recycling the Earth's water supply through the water cycle. Freshwater ecosystems are found in areas with differing temperatures and support a variety of animal and plant life.

The oceans, which have a high salinity level, comprise the **marine ecosystems**. Oceans contain saltwater and are the largest ecosystems on Earth. Marine ecosystems are divided into different zones depending on factors such as light availability and water depth. The zones of marine ecosystems are **intertidal**, **pelagic** and **benthic**.

Figure 15.7 Marine Ecosystem

The **intertidal** zone is the area of shore between low and high tides. It is the most biologically active area in a marine ecosystem with a high level of light and nutrients. Because of the high tides and shifting sand, this area is also under the most stress. Animals like sand crabs often move to find protection. Rocky shores provide good places for *kelp and invertebrates* to attach themselves, but these organisms also have to deal with changing water levels.

The largest ocean area is the **pelagic** zone, which is further divided into two areas. The more shallow area is closer to shore and has a maximum depth of 200 meters. There is good light for photosynthetic organisms in this shallow area. Many types of fish including *tuna, herring, sardines, sharks and rays* live in this area along with *whales and porpoises*. The deeper part of the pelagic zone comprises most of the oceans in the world. This area is deeper than 200 meters. It receives little light, has cold water temperatures and high pressure. Many different organisms are adapted to the various characteristics of the ocean depths. Some fish have no eyes or have developed luminescent organs. *Lantern fish, eels and grenadier fish* live in this area.

Figure 15.8 Coral Reef

The **benthic** zone is the ocean floor. Animals such as *worms, clams, hagfish, crabs and bacteria* can be found in deep benthic areas. In deep benthic areas, hydrothermal vents can form the basis of a complex food web supporting a variety of animals. Coral reefs are commonly found in the warm, shallow waters of benthic areas. The reefs prevent erosion and provide habitats for many organisms like *sea stars, plankton, sponges and a variety of fish*.

An **estuary** is a place where freshwater and saltwater meet in a coastal area. The salinity level in an estuary fluctuates, but is not as high as in the ocean ecosystems. The water is partly surrounded by land with access to open ocean and rivers. Estuaries contain salt marshes and swampy areas and are among the most biologically diverse locations on Earth. The diversity is attributed to the large amount of nutrients, the tides that circulate the nutrients and remove waste and the abundance of different types of plants.

Figure 15.9 Estuary

Activity

Create a comic book or story book about the different ecosystems found on Earth.

Chapter 15 Review

1. Tundra biomes generally occur near which latitudes?

    A. equatorial

    B. mid-continent

    C. middle

    D. polar

2. The eastern United States is predominately a

    A. grassland biome.

    B. desert biome.

    C. coniferous biome.

    D. deciduous biome.

3. Tropical rain forests

    A. have little to no rainfall.

    B. have a diversity of species.

    C. fluctuate greatly in yearly temperatures.

    D. are found at polar latitudes.

4. What are large land areas characterized by a dominant form of plant life and climate type called?

    A. ecosystems

    B. communities

    C. populations

    D. biomes

5. The place a particular species occupies within the community is also called a(n)

    A. niche.

    B. ecosystem.

    C. biome.

    D. population.

1. (A) (B) (C) (D)
2. (A) (B) (C) (D)
3. (A) (B) (C) (D)
4. (A) (B) (C) (D)
5. (A) (B) (C) (D)

Domain 2 Review

1. (A) (B) (C) (D)   11. (A) (B) (C) (D)
2. (A) (B) (C) (D)   12. (A) (B) (C) (D)
3. (A) (B) (C) (D)   13. (A) (B) (C) (D)
4. (A) (B) (C) (D)   14. (A) (B) (C) (D)
5. (A) (B) (C) (D)   15. (A) (B) (C) (D)
6. (A) (B) (C) (D)   16. (A) (B) (C) (D)
7. (A) (B) (C) (D)   17. (A) (B) (C) (D)
8. (A) (B) (C) (D)   18. (A) (B) (C) (D)
9. (A) (B) (C) (D)   19. (A) (B) (C) (D)
10. (A) (B) (C) (D)   20. (A) (B) (C) (D)

1. The area in which certain types of plants or animals can be found living in close proximity to each other is called a

   A. habitat.

   B. community.

   C. niche.

   D. kingdom.

2. The interactions of plants, animals and microorganisms with each other and with their environment constitutes a(n)

   A. niche.

   B. ecosystem.

   C. positive tropism.

   D. symbiotic relationship.

3. The relationship between two members of a community in which one member harms another by its presence is

   A. parasitism.

   B. commensalism.

   C. mutualism.

   D. dependency.

4. The _____ zone is the area of shore between low and high tides.

   A. deep

   B. benthic

   C. pelagic

   D. intertidal

5. The place where a member of a community lives and finds food is called its

   A. pond.

   B. biome.

   C. habitat.

   D. residence.

6. Specific regions of the Earth that have unique climate demands for living things are called

   A. biospheres.

   B. habitats.

   C. biomes.

   D. communities.

7. Fish in a pond are _____ in that community.

   A. producers

   B. a population

   C. unnecessary elements

   D. the habitat

8. Man-of-war fish cluster around the venomous tentacles of jellyfish to escape larger predators. The presence of the man-of-war fish does not harm or benefit the jellyfish. This type of relationship is

   A. parasitism.

   B. commensalism.

   C. succession.

   D. mutualism.

9. Each species in a community has its own _____, or place, as a member of the community.

    A. ecosystem

    B. niche

    C. habitat

    D. kingdom

10. _____ competition occurs between two members of the same species competing for the same resources.

    A. Intraspecies

    B. Community

    C. Commensal

    D. Interspecies

11. Photosynthesis is performed by

    A. omnivores.

    B. producers.

    C. secondary consumers.

    D. primary consumers.

12. A density-dependent factor

    A. limits a population in a given area regardless of size.

    B. limits the population when the population reaches a certain size.

    C. may include weather or a natural disaster.

    D. often affects small, sparse populations.

13. Things that restrict the growth of a population are called

    A. negative factors.

    B. selective factors.

    C. predators.

    D. limiting factors.

14. A population will grow if

    A. the immigration and emigration rates are equal, and births and deaths are equal.

    B. the immigration and emigration rates are equal and the number of deaths exceeds the number of births.

    C. the immigration and emigration rates are equal, and the number of births exceeds the number of deaths.

    D. the emigration rate is greater than the immigration rate, and births and deaths are equal.

15. The abiotic factors in an ecosystem are

    A. decomposers.

    B. living.

    C. non-living.

    D. photosynthetic.

16. Many types of bacteria obtain their nutrition from dead plants and animals and, in turn, recycle elements such as carbon and nitrogen. These bacteria are

    A. decomposers.

    B. producers.

    C. carnivores.

    D. viruses.

17. A symbiotic relationship means

    A. the energy cycle is not involved.

    B. no one benefits.

    C. the solar system is involved.

    D. one or both parties benefit.

18. Red foxes are nocturnal and live in meadows and forest edges. They are predators to small mammals, amphibians and insects. The scraps that red foxes leave behind provide food for scavengers and decomposers. The preceding sentences describe the red fox's

A. community.

B. prey.

C. niche.

D. food web.

19. The now-extinct dodo bird was a flightless bird, native to the island of Mauritius. It ate mainly fruit and nested on the ground. When humans arrived on Mauritius, they brought pigs, dogs, cats and monkeys, all of which ate dodo eggs. What is the most obvious explanation for its extinction?

A. The process of primary succession destroyed its food supply.

B. The dodo could not form a mutualistic relationship with another organism.

C. The dodo was unable to adapt to changing environmental conditions.

D. The dodo experienced a genetic mutation that killed them.

20. Omnivores are

A. producers.

B. primary consumers.

C. secondary consumers.

D. both primary and secondary consumers.

Domain 3
Evolution

Chapter 16: Physical Change   S7L5a

This chapter discusses how Darwin developed his ideas on evolution along
with examples of evolution, including the Galapagos finches and the peppered moths.

Chapter 17: Natural Selection   S7L5b

This chapter describes how evolution happens through natural selection,
mutations, gene flow and genetic drift. Also, patterns of evolution such as convergent,
divergent, adaptive radiation and co-evolution are discussed.

Chapter 18: Fossil Record   S7L5c

This chapter introduces the scientific support for the theory of evolution, with
topics like fossils and the fossil record. Other ideas covered in this chapter include relative
dating, index fossils and radiation measurement.

Make a Concept Map

Use the blank space here to develop your own concept map about topics in Domain 3. Complete this activity **before** beginning the domain to find out what you may already know about evolution! Then at the end of the domain return to your concept map and add or change things you learned in this section. Refer to **Appendix A**, if you need help.

Chapter 16
Physical Change

GEORGIA 7TH GRADE CRCT IN SCIENCE STANDARDS COVERED IN THIS CHAPTER INCLUDE:

S7L5a	Explain how physical characteristics of organism have changed over successive generations (e.g., Darwin's finches and peppered moths of Manchester).

CHANGE OVER TIME

Have you ever noticed all the different kinds of plant and animals in the world? Have you ever wondered how there came to be so many different kinds? Have you ever wanted to know how some animals can be so similar and still be so different? For example, think about an ostrich from Africa. Did you know that there is a bird in Australia called an emu that is very similar to an ostrich? An emu is different from an ostrich in size and color but both are large, flightless birds that occupy the same niche in the environment. In this section, we will examine how plant and animal populations change over time.

During the 1800s, people became interested in scientifically studying the natural world. The British commissioned many scientific expeditions all around the world. One such expedition was the trip of the HMS Beagle. In 1831, the Beagle left England on a scientific journey. One man on this ship was **Charles Darwin**. Darwin was the ship naturalist and was responsible for collecting plant and animal samples from around the world.

Figure 16.1 Galapagos Island Satellite View

Darwin visited many places and studied plants, animals and fossils from locations all around the world, including the Galapagos Islands. The **Galapagos Islands** are located off the coast of South America. The islands have different climates, one is dry while others get lots of rain.

Figure 16.2 Galapagos on the Globe

DARWIN'S FINCHES

Darwin noticed that the birds on the Galapagos looked similar to the finches on the South American continent. A finch is a kind of seed-eating bird. Every bird Darwin saw on the Galapagos Islands was a type of modified finch. The finches were about the same size and all very similar in color.

The only differences in the finches Darwin saw were their beaks and what kind of food they ate. There were finches that ate insects, seeds, plant matter, egg yolks and blood. The finches on the Galapagos Islands looked very similar to one type of finch on the South American continent, but none of the Galapagos Island finches were found on the South American mainland.

Figure 16.3 Darwin

Darwin theorized that all the island finches were offspring of one type of mainland finch that might have been blown to the Galapagos Islands during a storm. The population of finches was changing over time because of their environment. The process through which organisms change over time is called **adaptation**. Thousands of adaptations lead to the process of **evolution**.

The diet of the Galapagos finches changed in response to their new environment. There was a change of eating habits because there were limited food resources on the islands. Some physical traits may also be changed over time. As the finches began to eat different types of food, the way their beaks worked and looked began to change. Finches that began to eat insects needed longer beaks for digging beetles out of their burrows. Finches that ate seeds or nuts required thicker beaks to crack the seed shells.

How did the finches change their beaks in response to these needs? Scientists now view the process of natural selection like this: The finches' beaks did not change overnight, but rather over many, many generations. Among the population of beetle-eating finches, those that were born with longer, sharper beaks naturally had access to more beetles than those finches with shorter beaks. The sharp-beaked insect eating finches thrived, and had many offspring, while the short-beaked insect eating finches gradually died out. The sharp beak was a trait that

Figure 16.4 Types of Finch

was, in effect, *selected* by nature to thrive. The same thing happened in each finch population, until finches from a given population began to look similar to each other and different than other finches.

To be clear: the individual physical traits of a finch are not modified by the finch (his beak does not grow and change to suit his changing needs). Rather, the finches who were born with the trait that is favored by the current environmental pressures survive and pass that trait on to their offspring. This ensures that, over time, the expression of the favored trait becomes more pronounced, and other traits disappear.

PEPPERED MOTHS

Another example of how organisms change over time is with peppered moths of England. There are two basic types of peppered moth. A light-colored variety and a dark-colored variety. Birds are the main predator of moths using mostly eyesight to capture their prey.

Figure 16.5 Light and Dark Colored Pepper Moths

In the beginning of the 19th century, birch trees in England had white or light-colored bark and the most common form of peppered moth was the light-colored one. The light-colored moth was easily hidden on the light-colored birch tree.

The industrial revolution soon caused soot to cover the birch tree's bark, changing the bark color to black. Over the next few years, the most common form of peppered moth slowly changed to become the dark-colored one. The dark-colored moth was easily hidden on the dark-colored birch tree.

SHOWING ORGANISM RELATIONSHIPS

There are several ways scientists organize information. One way scientists show the evolutionary relationships between organisms is with a **cladogram**, or branching tree. A cladogram is a graphical tool scientists use to show the relatedness of organisms. When making a cladogram, scientists use genetic relatedness, organism structures and special features of the organisms' lifecycle. The gain or loss of characteristics in organisms causes the "tree" to branch. The organisms then form the "leaves" of the tree. Figure 16.6 shows a sample cladogram.

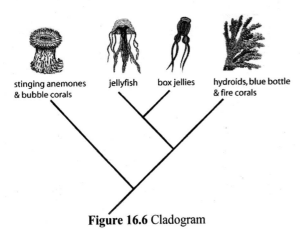

Figure 16.6 Cladogram

Think of the image as a family tree. The main trunk of the cladogram is where the oldest ancestor or acquired trait is located. Each "branch" represents a common ancestor or newly developed trait among the organisms listed.

A branch located near the top of the tree contains a young ancestor (or trait) while a branch closer to the main trunk contains a more distant ancestor (or trait). Organisms located close to one another (on the same branch) are more related while organisms located far apart (on different branches) are less related. In Figure 16.6, stinging anemones and fire corals are distant ancesters while jellyfish and box jellyfish are closely related.

Some cladograms list the changing characteristics along the branches while others do not. Examine the sample cladogram in Figure 16.7 and determine the most closely related organisms and the most distantly related organisms.

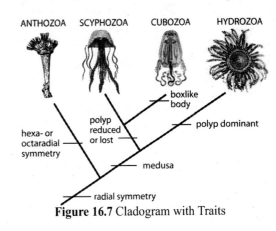

Figure 16.7 Cladogram with Traits

Activity

Make a cladogram for organisms from one of the six kingdoms. Then collect pictures of the organisms and attach them to your cladogram.

Chapter 16 Review

1. How did Darwin develop his ideas about evolution?

   A. by studying plants, animals and fossil remains around the world aboard the HMS Beagle

   B. by studying only fossil remains found on different continents around the world

   C. by watching peppered moths change from white to black

   D. by making thousands of cladograms

2. What type of animal MOST contributed to Darwin's ideas on evolution?

   A. peppered moths

   B. Galapagos finches

   C. Galapagos turtles

   D. marine iguanas

3. The main idea of evolution states that

   A. the characteristics of organisms within a population change over time.

   B. only the best organisms survive.

   C. the characteristics of organisms can change during their lifetime.

   D. organisms can survive in any environment on Earth.

The image below is a cladogram, or branching tree. This diagram shows how different kinds of plants are related.

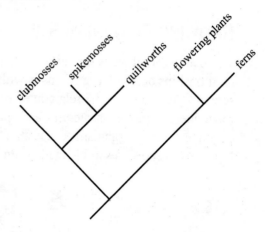

4. Can you select the two most closely related types of plants?

   A. clubmosses and quillworths

   B. spikemosses and ferns

   C. quillworths and flowering plants

   D. flowering plants and ferns

5. Which physical feature helped Darwin develop his ideas on evolution?

   A. tortoise shell size

   B. color of peppered moths

   C. behavior of finches

   D. shape of beaks on finches

1. Ⓐ Ⓑ Ⓒ Ⓓ
2. Ⓐ Ⓑ Ⓒ Ⓓ
3. Ⓐ Ⓑ Ⓒ Ⓓ
4. Ⓐ Ⓑ Ⓒ Ⓓ
5. Ⓐ Ⓑ Ⓒ Ⓓ

Chapter 17
Natural Selection

GEORGIA 7TH GRADE CRCT IN SCIENCE STANDARDS COVERED IN THIS CHAPTER INCLUDE:

S7L5b	Describe ways in which species on earth have evolved due to natural selection.

Figure 17.1 Miniature Horses

Recall that selective breeding is a process where humans artificially breed plants or animals to show specific traits. Remember that breeding successively smaller horses will eventually produce a miniature horse. In this way, humans determine the desired traits of plants or animals. This process is often called **artificial selection**.

HOW EVOLUTION HAPPENS

NATURAL SELECTION

Darwin had repeatedly observed that environmental pressures can change how an organism naturally interacts with its environment. He developed a theory based on these observations and called it **the theory of natural selection**. The theory of natural selection states that the organisms best suited to the environment will most likely survive to produce many offspring.

Darwin realized that organisms must compete for resources like food, water and space and that most organisms produce more offspring than the environment can support. The organisms that can perform the best are most likely to get the food, water or space and will live a long life. Remember the beetle-eating finches on the Galapagos? The finches that had longer, sharper beaks were able to get more food faster than the finches with short, stubby beaks. This meant that finches with long sharp beaks made up more of the next generation.

Recall that sexual reproduction produces organisms with slightly different characteristics. As a result, not all individuals within a population are exactly alike. Some prey animals have better hearing and eyesight and are able to escape predators easily. These different characteristics, or **adaptations**, determine the probability of an organisms' survival. Any inherited trait is called an adaptation. Adaptations can be physical, chemical or behavioral.

Scientists call the ability of an organism to live, survive and reproduce in a particular environment **fitness**. Not all individual animals within a population have the same fitness. The natural variation produced through sexual reproduction makes some organisms more fit than others. This is where the idea of **survival of the fittest** comes from.

Here is an example: Bears in the Arctic may have had a variety of colors.

As the bear population began to grow, they competed for limited prey.

Some bears were born with mutations that caused their fur to be lighter in color. The light-colored bears were better able to catch more prey than the darker-colored bears. As a result, the light-colored bears had more offspring and passed along the trait for light color to the next generation.

Figure 17.2 Polar Bear Shades

The dark-colored polar bears eventually died off, leaving only light-colored polar bears.

Keep in mind that a favorable adaptation in one environment may not be favorable in a different environment. Many deep ocean-dwelling invertebrates are red in color because red light waves cannot penetrate to the ocean depths. The red color helps the animals "disappear" into the ocean. If these invertebrates were moved to a shallow environment, they would be easily seen and eaten by predators.

Another example is a snow leopard (*Panthera uncia*). This leopard lives in the high mountains of Central Asia, mostly the Himalaya Mountains. This leopard has a light, grayish-white coat to hide from prey. If this leopard were found on the African plains, it would easily stand out and probably not catch any prey. However, if the environment in Africa changed, and snow became common, it is likely that most African predators would develop light, snow-colored coats. Remember that change takes place over many generations and favorable adaptations are more likely to be passed on to offspring.

Recall that physical traits are formed by combinations of genes. Changes in genes can cause changes in populations of plants and animals. Some ways that genes change and affect the appearance of a population are mutations, gene flow and genetic drift.

MUTATIONS

Mutations are random changes in DNA that act as another way organisms evolve. These changes result in a variation in traits, which then pass from one generation to the next. Mutations can be beneficial, neutral or harmful to an organism. Mutations beneficial to the organism in a particular environment lead to furthering of the species. For example, a mutation in color pigments can lead to an individual that is a different color than the normal population. Remember the orange carrots from Chapter 10?

Figure 17.3 Many Hues of Carrots

GENE FLOW

Gene flow is the change in the occurrence of genes in a population. **Population** refers to the group of organisms of the same species in a given geographic area. Gene flow can occur when an individual leaves a population or a new individual joins a population. Gene flow tends to increase similarities of populations since individuals from different populations share their genes with each other through reproduction. Gene flow happens easily in plants that have seeds carried by wind. The wind carries the seeds of a plant from one population to another population. When these new seeds grow into plants, the plants can cross-pollinate with the existing plants, leading to the sharing of genes from different populations.

GENETIC DRIFT

Genetic drift provides random changes in the occurrence of genes through chance events. These chance events can take place when a few individuals of a population break off from the original group and start their own population, also known as the **founder effect**. This is what happened with Darwin's finches. A few birds might have been blown to the Galapagos Islands during a storm. These "founder" birds remained on the island and reproduced, eventually developing into different species.

Figure 17.4 Bottlenecking

Genetic drift can also occur if a large number of the population is killed because of disease, starvation, change in natural environment or a natural disaster. When this happens to a population, it is called **bottlenecking**. A large population is reduced to a few individuals, and the genes of subsequent generations become very similar. Inbreeding between these few individuals leads to populations that have very few genetic differences. This situation happens with many endangered species like the Florida panther (*Puma concolor coryi*). Many panthers were killed by human hunters or died because of habitat loss. This has created a modern bottleneck. This bottleneck is suspected to be the reason why many Florida panthers have breeding problems.

Figure 17.5 The Florida Panther

PATTERNS OF EVOLUTION

The theory of evolution suggests that there is more than one way to evolve or change. These different patterns provide different paths to explain the degree of change among organisms. Some ways that organisms are thought to evolve include convergent evolution, divergent evolution and co-evolution.

CONVERGENT EVOLUTION

Figure 17.6 The Monarch Butterfly

Figure 17.7
The Small Brown Bat

Convergent evolution explains how unrelated species can develop similar characteristics. Convergent evolution is demonstrated through the bat and the butterfly. The bat is a mammal and the butterfly is an insect. These two unrelated animals share similar characteristics that suit their environment: broad, flat wings. The wing of a bat and a butterfly look similar and function in much the same way.

DIVERGENT EVOLUTION

Divergent evolution suggests that many species develop from a common ancestor. The different species adapt to their particular environments. For instance, grizzly bears and polar bears are both bears. Grizzly bears are brown and adapted to life in a temperate climate whereas polar bears are white and adapted to a polar climate. The grizzly bear and the polar bear *diverged* from a common ancestor.

CO-EVOLUTION

Co-evolution happens when two or more organisms in an ecosystem change in response to each other. Co-evolution is believed to occur frequently with flowers and their pollinators. Hummingbirds have long, narrow beaks, an attraction to the color red and a poor sense of smell. The fuchsia plant, whose flowers bloom in various shades of red, give off little smell and have long, narrow flowers. Fuchsias rely on hummingbirds as their pollinators. Over time, the red-flowered fuchsias and the long-beaked hummingbirds have had great success as partners in survival.

Figure 17.8 Hummingbird

Activity

For this activity you will need a multicolored fabric or paper (floral wall paper, Hawaiian shirts or drawer liner works well), paper chips of different colored construction paper (these can be made using a hole puncher) and students. Divide the students into groups of three or four.

Each group will make their paper chips by punching holes from different colored construction paper (black, white, red, green, yellow, white, pink or any other color). Each group will need an "environment" (multicolored background), 50 – 100 different colored paper chips, two student "hunters" and one student timer.

Place a handful of paper chips in the environment and allow the hunters to hunt for 20 – 45 seconds. Then locate the surviving paper chips and add two chips for each one that survived in the environment. Repeat the hunting and replacing of chips several times.

In this activity, what was the prey? What trait was different among the prey? What did you notice about the traits of the prey during the game? Why were prey chips placed back into the environment?

You can repeat this activity using plain colored backgrounds (like construction paper) to see the effect on prey. What do you predict will happen to the different prey traits on a plain colored background?

Repeat the activity and change the feeding habits of students by allowing one to use sticky tape on their fingers and the other gloves or oven mitts. Predict the changes in hunters and prey items.

Chapter 17 Review

1. One very important mechanism for evolution is genetic drift, which is the

   A. random change in genes within a population.

   B. formation of new species.

   C. evolution of two species in response to each other.

   D. ability of an organism to survive in its environment.

2. Which of the following are patterns of evolution?

   A. structural replication, reproductive homology and special creation

   B. metabolic pathways, hormonal indicators and genetic studies

   C. modern creationism, fossil theory and punctuational model

   D. convergent evolution and co-evolution

3. If two organisms evolve in response to each other, which evolutionary pattern is demonstrated?

   A. natural selection

   B. gradualistic method

   C. co-evolution

   D. adaptive radiation

4. Tortoises are land-dwelling turtles that can survive in a variety of environments. Sea turtles are turtles that are adapted to life in the ocean. Which pattern of evolution is demonstrated by these two animals?

   A. convergent evolution

   B. divergent evolution

   C. co-evolution

   D. adaptive radiation

5. The ability of an organism to survive and reproduce in an environment is called its

   A. evolution.

   B. natural selection.

   C. bottleneck.

   D. fitness.

1. (A) (B) (C) (D)
2. (A) (B) (C) (D)
3. (A) (B) (C) (D)
4. (A) (B) (C) (D)
5. (A) (B) (C) (D)

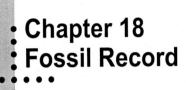

Chapter 18
Fossil Record

GEORGIA 7TH GRADE CRCT IN SCIENCE STANDARDS COVERED IN THIS CHAPTER INCLUDE:

S7L5c	Explain how the fossil record found in sedimentary rock provides evidence for the long history of changing life forms.

THE FOSSIL RECORD

Fossils also provide evidence for the change in organisms over time. A **fossil** is the recognizable remains or body impressions of an organism that lived in the past. The **fossil record** refers to all fossils that have been found since the study of fossils began. Fossils can be used to show how organisms have changed or evolved over time.

For instance, Figure 18.1 shows the evolution of the modern horse from the Eocene (about 60 million years ago) to modern times.

Hyracotherium was the earliest identifiable ancestor to the horse. This animal was about the size of a fox. It lived in the forest and ate foliage (leaves of trees and bushes) and fruits. The environment soon began to change into a prairie-like grassland. Over the next few million years, you can see that the animal grew taller (to see over the grasses), developed longer legs (to out-run predators) and developed tougher teeth (to eat grasses). The modern horse is much different than its tiny ancestor.

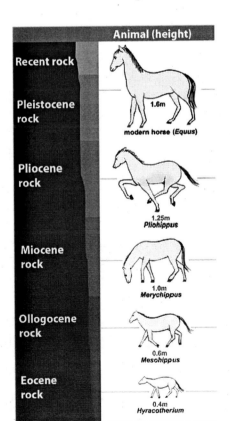

Figure 18.1 Evolution of the Horse

Fossils are found in sedimentary rock. Recall from earth science that **sedimentary rock** is formed when other types of rock are broken down and re-deposited somewhere else. Sedimentary rocks are usually layered. The oldest rock layers are found on the bottom, while the newer rock layers are located near the top.

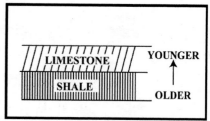

Figure 18.2 Superposition

The formation of sedimentary rock usually involves four processes: weathering, transportation, deposition and compaction. Sedimentary rock can be formed from the particles carried by rivers, lakes, oceans, glaciers or winds. Their compaction into rocks usually occurs without any drastic temperature elevation. For this reason, many living tissues, or the impressions of living tissues, can last through the process. Minerals within the organism are replaced and the once-living tissue becomes rock.

There are many processes on the Earth's surface that break down and destroy living tissue. Plants and animals rot and become food for other living creatures. (Remember the decomposers like fungi and bacteria?)

Fossils are also more likely to form when animals are buried by dirt or ash very quickly. Events like floods, earthquakes, mud slides and ash deposition from volcanoes are more likely to preserve tissues. Like buried treasure, organisms can remain untouched in the earth for millions of years.

For these reasons, fossils are very rare, and each one is very important to scientists. In fact, some scientists estimate that the fossil record only represents about **0.1%** of all the organisms that have lived on the planet! It is important to remember that no one knows exactly how many plants and animals have lived or do currently live on Earth.

DETERMINING AGE

Fossils are useful in determining the age of rocks. There are two basic ways fossils are used to determine the age of rocks: relative dating and absolute dating.

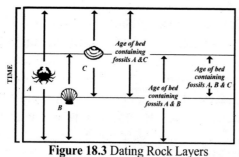

Figure 18.3 Dating Rock Layers

Relative dating is done through the use of index fossils and sedimentary rock layers. Fossils recognized as unique to certain time periods are called **index fossils**. When an index fossil is found in a layer of sedimentary rock, the age of the rock is assumed to be the same as the age of the fossil. Generally speaking, the older the layer, the greater the difference of the organism from today's species. Relative dating is useful to tell how old one fossil is when compared to another fossil.

RADIATION MEASUREMENT

When scientists use fossils and rock strata to study geologic time, they are using relative measurements, meaning that age is determined by the relative order in which they appear. This may seem to be inexact or too approximate. Don't worry, there IS a method of geologic dating that is much more exact. It uses the natural decay of **radioactive isotopes** (special types of atoms) that "fall apart" on predictable time schedules. Unstable isotopes, called **radioactive parents**, decay and form other more stable elements, called **daughter**

products. This decay happens at a measurable rate. The calculation of the ratio of parent to daughter products (how many you have of one, compared to how many you have of the other) is known as radiometric dating.

We know how long it should take for unstable atoms to decay and give way to stable ones. The time it takes for one-half of the original, unstable atoms to decay into the daughter product is called **half-life**. To put it another way, half-life is the time required for one-half of the parent isotope in a rock to decay into a daughter product. The table below shows the most frequently used isotopes in radiometric dating.

Table 18.1 Radioactive Decay of Some Commonly Used Dating Isotopes

Radioactive Parent	Daughter Product	Half-Life
Uranium-238	Lead-206	4 – 5 billion years
Thorium-232	Lead-206	14.1 billion years
Rubidium-87	Strontium-87	47.0 billion years
Potassium-40	Argon-40	1.3 billion years
Carbon-14	Nitrogen-14	5,730 years

Figure 18.4 illustrates how half-life works. When animals are alive, they take in small amounts of radioactive elements. When the animal dies, it stops taking in radioactive elements. Since the radioactive isotope contained in the organism decays at a predictable rate, counting the atoms of the daughter product gives an indication of the time elapsed since the organism died. Here is an example. Let's say a deceased animal contains a million atoms of the parent isotope with a half-life of five million years. At this point, we will assume that the number of daughter product atoms is zero.

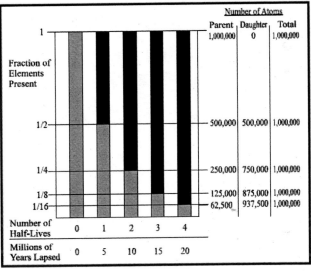

Figure 18.4 Half-Life

The second bar shows the change in radioactive isotope and daughter products at the end of the first half-life (which we already told you is 5 million years). Half of the parent isotopes have now decayed into daughter products, so there are now 500,000 atoms of the parent isotope and 500,000 atoms of daughter product.

Going forward another five million years to the third bar, another half-life has passed, and the number of atoms of the parent isotope left after the end of the first half-life has now been reduced by half to 250,000 atoms, while the amount of daughter product has increased by 250,000 atoms to 750,000.

At the end of the fourth half-life, twenty million years from the starting point, the parent isotope count is 62,500 and the daughter count is 937,500. If a geologist found this fossil now, he could determine the total number of parent and daughter isotopes back in the lab, and knowing the half-life of the parent, he could work backwards to calculate an absolute date of twenty million years for the rock!

Even though radiometric dating is more reliable, it does not always produce undisputed ages of fossils and rocks. Using radiometric dating requires scientists to make several assumptions that may or may not be correct. First, radiometric dating assumes that the decay of radioactive elements is not affected by the external environment. Second, it assumes the sample was isolated so that no parent or daughter isotopes were lost or added over time. Since we cannot guarantee both of these assumptions to be true, we have to accept that there is at least some margin of error in the process.

Chapter 18 Review

1. A fossil recognized as unique to a certain time period is known as

   A. an index fossil.

   B. a distinct fossil.

   C. a time marker fossil.

   D. a marker fossil.

2. One event that does not lead to fossil formation is

   A. floods.

   B. forest fires.

   C. earthquakes.

   D. mudslides.

3. It is difficult for fossils of cells to be found because

   A. none exist.

   B. humans cannot dig deep enough into the earth.

   C. no catastrophic events occurred in the ecosystems of the early Earth.

   D. cells have no hard parts that will fossil-ize.

4. Absolute dating

   A. produces undisputed ages of fossils.

   B. produces the exact age of fossils.

   C. uses radioactive decay to determine the age of fossils.

   D. is useful to correlate the age of one fossil to that of another.

5. Fossils are useful

   A. in determining how species have changed over time.

   B. in determining the absolute age of rock layers only.

   C. to scientists only.

   D. to students only.

1. Ⓐ Ⓑ Ⓒ Ⓓ
2. Ⓐ Ⓑ Ⓒ Ⓓ
3. Ⓐ Ⓑ Ⓒ Ⓓ
4. Ⓐ Ⓑ Ⓒ Ⓓ
5. Ⓐ Ⓑ Ⓒ Ⓓ

Domain 3 Review

1. Ⓐ Ⓑ Ⓒ Ⓓ

2. Ⓐ Ⓑ Ⓒ Ⓓ

3. Ⓐ Ⓑ Ⓒ Ⓓ

4. Ⓐ Ⓑ Ⓒ Ⓓ

5. Ⓐ Ⓑ Ⓒ Ⓓ

6. Ⓐ Ⓑ Ⓒ Ⓓ

7. Ⓐ Ⓑ Ⓒ Ⓓ

8. Ⓐ Ⓑ Ⓒ Ⓓ

9. Ⓐ Ⓑ Ⓒ Ⓓ

10. Ⓐ Ⓑ Ⓒ Ⓓ

11. Ⓐ Ⓑ Ⓒ Ⓓ

12. Ⓐ Ⓑ Ⓒ Ⓓ

13. Ⓐ Ⓑ Ⓒ Ⓓ

14. Ⓐ Ⓑ Ⓒ Ⓓ

15. Ⓐ Ⓑ Ⓒ Ⓓ

16. Ⓐ Ⓑ Ⓒ Ⓓ

17. Ⓐ Ⓑ Ⓒ Ⓓ

18. Ⓐ Ⓑ Ⓒ Ⓓ

19. Ⓐ Ⓑ Ⓒ Ⓓ

20. Ⓐ Ⓑ Ⓒ Ⓓ

1. Use the chart below to determine which element would be the best choice to determine the age of an object suspected to be less than 40,000 years old.

Radioactive Parent	Daughter Product	Half-Life
Uranium-238	Lead-206	4 – 5 billion years
Thorium-232	Lead-206	14.1 billion years
Rubidium-87	Strontium-87	47.0 billion years
Potassium-40	Argon-40	1.3 billion years
Carbon-14	Nitrogen-14	5,730 years

    A. Uranium-238

    B. Thorium-232

    C. Potassium-40

    D. Carbon-14

2. The time required for half of a parent isotope to decay into a daughter product is known as

    A. half-life.

    B. measurable rate.

    C. parent-to-daughter reduction.

    D. isotopic enumeration.

3. Radioactive elements change into other elements by

    A. molecular collision.

    B. decay.

    C. combustion.

    D. reduction.

4. Radioactive decay

    A. occurs at a predictable rate.

    B. speeds up when temperature rises.

    C. slows when pressure is added.

    D. occurs only in the Sun.

5. Natural selection states that individuals

    A. best suited to the environment will most likely survive to produce many offspring.

    B. on the bottom level of a hierarchy have the greatest reproductive success.

    C. demonstrating altruistic behavior are the ones with the most mutations.

    D. remain unchanged over a period of time.

6. A mountain, ocean or ravine divides a population. After many years, the separated organisms show genetic differences from the original population. Which of the following explains how this change occurred?

    A. convergent selection

    B. natural selection

    C. co-evolution

    D. parallel evolution

7. The arctic fox and red fox are examples of

    A. co-evolution.

    B. convergent evolution.

    C. divergent evolution.

    D. parallel evolution.

Use the figure to answer questions 10 and 11

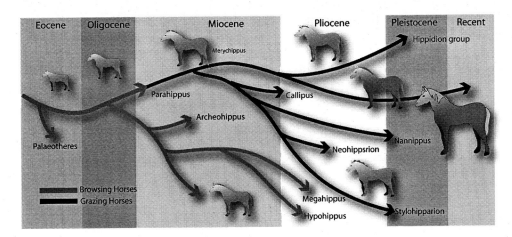

8. Certain insects and plants evolve in tandem. This is an example of

   A. co-evolution.

   B. convergent evolution.

   C. divergent evolution.

   D. parallel evolution.

9. Sharks and whales are an example of

   A. co-evolution.

   B. convergent evolution.

   C. divergent evolution.

   D. parallel evolution.

Refer to the figure above to answer questions 10 and 11

10. Many years ago Hyracotherium was a forest-dwelling creature that ate soft foliage and fruit. Over time, this animal changed into the modern horse, Equus. What mechanism caused this animal to change?

    A. natural selection

    B. mutation

    C. speciation

    D. germination

11. Which statement best describes how Hyracotherium changed into the modern horse?

    A. Environmental pressures reduced the food supply, which encouraged the co-evolution of a larger species.

    B. New environmental pressures selected an animal that was tall, could run fast and had tough teeth.

    C. Old environmental pressures caused a divergent species to develop.

    D. Hyracotherium became extinct, causing the other species of horse to develop.

12. The mixing of gene pools

    A. promotes diversity.

    B. increases the number of organisms.

    C. reduces the number of organisms.

    D. reduces diversity.

13. While aboard the HMS Beagle, Darwin started thinking about

    A. how species changed over time.

    B. how animals colonized small islands.

    C. how to sail a ship around the world.

    D. the peppered moths of Manchester.

14. According to Darwin,

   A. animals only pass down traits they have acquired during their lifetime to their offspring.

   B. animals must acquire traits favored by environmental conditions during their lifetime, to survive.

   C. animals that are born with traits favored by environmental conditions are more likely to survive, and pass down those traits to offspring.

   D. animals that are born with unusual traits never survive, and will not pass down those traits to offspring.

15. The fossil record

   A. only represents a small fraction of life that has existed on Earth.

   B. represents a complete record of all the organisms that have lived on Earth.

   C. is a hoax developed by scientists.

   D. represents a moderate amount of the history of life on Earth.

16. Pitcher plants and Venus flytraps are two unrelated plant species that live in nutrient-poor soil. Both types of plants trap and eat animals to help obtain nutrients needed for life. This is an example of

   A. co-evolution.

   B. convergent evolution.

   C. divergent evolution.

   D. parallel evolution.

17. The great diversity seen among domesticated dogs is a result of

   A. artificial selection.

   B. natural selection.

   C. co-evolution.

   D. natural fitness.

18. When developing his ideas on natural selection, Darwin realized

   A. that only the strong survive.

   B. that organisms that are the most fit will survive.

   C. that humans are better able to breed perfect organisms.

   D. organisms develop physical adaptations during their lifetime.

19. How do the Galapagos finches contribute to ideas on evolution?

   A. They showed Darwin only about adaptive radiation.

   B. They show how artificial selection produces many species from one species.

   C. They show how natural selection can produce many species from one species.

   D. They showed humans about co-evolution.

20. Why is a bottleneck bad for a population?

   A. It reduces genetic diversity and can lead to inbreeding.

   B. It increases genetic diversity and can lead to inbreeding.

   C. It always causes reproductive problems.

   D. It is an adaptive radiation.

Georgia 7th Grade CRCT
Post Test 1

Post Test 1   **Answer Sheet**

Name: _____

Section 1

1. Ⓐ Ⓑ Ⓒ Ⓓ
2. Ⓐ Ⓑ Ⓒ Ⓓ
3. Ⓐ Ⓑ Ⓒ Ⓓ
4. Ⓐ Ⓑ Ⓒ Ⓓ
5. Ⓐ Ⓑ Ⓒ Ⓓ
6. Ⓐ Ⓑ Ⓒ Ⓓ
7. Ⓐ Ⓑ Ⓒ Ⓓ
8. Ⓐ Ⓑ Ⓒ Ⓓ
9. Ⓐ Ⓑ Ⓒ Ⓓ
10. Ⓐ Ⓑ Ⓒ Ⓓ
11. Ⓐ Ⓑ Ⓒ Ⓓ
12. Ⓐ Ⓑ Ⓒ Ⓓ
13. Ⓐ Ⓑ Ⓒ Ⓓ
14. Ⓐ Ⓑ Ⓒ Ⓓ
15. Ⓐ Ⓑ Ⓒ Ⓓ
16. Ⓐ Ⓑ Ⓒ Ⓓ
17. Ⓐ Ⓑ Ⓒ Ⓓ
18. Ⓐ Ⓑ Ⓒ Ⓓ
19. Ⓐ Ⓑ Ⓒ Ⓓ
20. Ⓐ Ⓑ Ⓒ Ⓓ
21. Ⓐ Ⓑ Ⓒ Ⓓ

22. Ⓐ Ⓑ Ⓒ Ⓓ
23. Ⓐ Ⓑ Ⓒ Ⓓ
24. Ⓐ Ⓑ Ⓒ Ⓓ
25. Ⓐ Ⓑ Ⓒ Ⓓ
26. Ⓐ Ⓑ Ⓒ Ⓓ
27. Ⓐ Ⓑ Ⓒ Ⓓ
28. Ⓐ Ⓑ Ⓒ Ⓓ
29. Ⓐ Ⓑ Ⓒ Ⓓ
30. Ⓐ Ⓑ Ⓒ Ⓓ

Section 2

31. Ⓐ Ⓑ Ⓒ Ⓓ
32. Ⓐ Ⓑ Ⓒ Ⓓ
33. Ⓐ Ⓑ Ⓒ Ⓓ
34. Ⓐ Ⓑ Ⓒ Ⓓ
35. Ⓐ Ⓑ Ⓒ Ⓓ
36. Ⓐ Ⓑ Ⓒ Ⓓ
37. Ⓐ Ⓑ Ⓒ Ⓓ
38. Ⓐ Ⓑ Ⓒ Ⓓ
39. Ⓐ Ⓑ Ⓒ Ⓓ
40. Ⓐ Ⓑ Ⓒ Ⓓ

41. Ⓐ Ⓑ Ⓒ Ⓓ
42. Ⓐ Ⓑ Ⓒ Ⓓ
43. Ⓐ Ⓑ Ⓒ Ⓓ
44. Ⓐ Ⓑ Ⓒ Ⓓ
45. Ⓐ Ⓑ Ⓒ Ⓓ
46. Ⓐ Ⓑ Ⓒ Ⓓ
47. Ⓐ Ⓑ Ⓒ Ⓓ
48. Ⓐ Ⓑ Ⓒ Ⓓ
49. Ⓐ Ⓑ Ⓒ Ⓓ
50. Ⓐ Ⓑ Ⓒ Ⓓ
51. Ⓐ Ⓑ Ⓒ Ⓓ
52. Ⓐ Ⓑ Ⓒ Ⓓ
53. Ⓐ Ⓑ Ⓒ Ⓓ
54. Ⓐ Ⓑ Ⓒ Ⓓ
55. Ⓐ Ⓑ Ⓒ Ⓓ
56. Ⓐ Ⓑ Ⓒ Ⓓ
57. Ⓐ Ⓑ Ⓒ Ⓓ
58. Ⓐ Ⓑ Ⓒ Ⓓ
59. Ⓐ Ⓑ Ⓒ Ⓓ
60. Ⓐ Ⓑ Ⓒ Ⓓ

Session 1

1. Two types of passive transport include   S7L2a

    A. diffusion and osmosis.

    B. diffusion and exocytosis.

    C. exocytosis and endocytosis.

    D. osmosis and endocytosis.

2. What is the final step in the scientific process?   S7CS9b

    A. conduct research

    B. do an experiment

    C. collect data

    D. draw a conclusion

3. The circulatory system interacts with what other body systems?   S7L2e

    A. the digestive and immune only

    B. the digestive, lymphatic and immune only

    C. the digestive, respiratory, lymphatic and immune only

    D. the circulatory system interacts with all the other body systems

4. What kind of alleles are present in the homozygous genotype?   S7L3a

    A. two recessive alleles

    B. two dominant alleles

    C. two identical alleles

    D. two non-identical alleles

5. Chipmunks eat grain, nuts, birds' eggs, fungi, worms and insects. How would you classify a chipmunk?   S7L4a

    A. herbivore   C. omnivore

    B. carnivore   D. scavenger

6. A labradoodle is a dog produced by crossing a pure-breed Labrador with a pure-breed poodle. This type of breeding is called   S7L3c

    A. cloning.

    B. genetic engineering.

    C. inbreeding.

    D. hybridization.

7. An African elephant (*Loxodonta africana*) population has few members and reproduces once every 22 – 24 months. How would this elephant population survive in a suddenly changed environment?   S7L4c

    A. The elephant population would adapt quickly to the change and survive.

    B. The elephant population would not adapt quickly to the change and possibly become endangered or extinct.

    C. The elephant population would not adapt at all to the change and would survive.

    D. The elephant population would adapt to the change and would become endangered or extinct.

8. According to Darwin, how did the Galapagos finches most likely arrive on the island archipelago?   S7L5a

    A. They were carried there by humans.

    B. They were blown there by a storm.

    C. They flew there by themselves.

    D. None of the above

Please go on to the next page

9. New penguin members join a population, as shown below. The population has a _____ growth rate. [S7L4c]

A. positive

C. neutral

B. negative

D. unlimited

10. Anglerfish live in the deep sea. Very little light reaches the depths where anglerfish live. To lure prey close, many species of anglerfish have a glowing limb to attract prey. This limb glows because of a special relationship the fish has with bacteria. How would you classify this kind of relationship? [S7L4d]

A. symbiotic

B. predatory

C. competitive

D. detrimental

11. If a human blood cell were placed in an isotonic sugar solution and left overnight what would most likely happen to the blood cell? [S7L2a]

A. nothing

B. it would swell and burst

C. it would shrivel and die

D. first it would swell then it would remain the same size

12. Humpback whales (*Megaptera novaeangliae*) and Steller Sea Lions (*Eumetopias jubatus*) both hunt and eat herring. The humpback whale and the sea lion have what type of relationship? [S7L4d]

A. competitive   C. predatory

B. mutualistic   D. commensalistic

13. Locate the answer that groups the correct type of cell with the correct type of cell division. [S7L3b]

A. reproductive cells use mitosis and somatic cells use meiosis.

B. reproductive cells use meiosis and somatic cells use mitosis.

C. reproductive cells use crossing over and somatic cells use meiosis.

D. somatic cells use crossing over and reproductive cells use mitosis.

14. A seventh-grade student goes to visit his cousin. After arriving, the student observes strangler figs, orchids, primates and sloths. What biome is this student most likely visiting? [S7L4e]

A. tundra

B. deciduous forest

C. grassland

D. rainforest

Please go on to the next page

15. Use the cladogram below to select the two most closely related organisms.   S7L5a

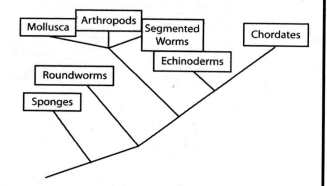

A. sponges and chordates

B. echinoderms and sponges

C. arthropods and segmented worms

D. roundworms and echinoderms

16. Randy is sick with the flu, and has large swollen glands in his neck. What system is most likely causing the swelling?   S7L2e

A. the nervous   C. the lymphatic

B. the skeletal   D. the muscular

17. Divergent evolution is   S7L5b

A. the belief that many new species can evolve from one common ancestor.

B. the process of gene alterations to a particular species.

C. the process of a species developing to look similar to a preexisting one.

D. what occurs when a species develops a new trait.

18. What is one reason why fossils are so rare?   S7L5c

A. Because there are many processes on Earth that destroy living tissue.

B. Because the Earth has not had many organisms living on it.

C. Because the Earth is very young.

D. Because humans destroy all the fossils they can find.

19. On an expedition into the Australian outback, a scientists discovers an interesting insect. Which tool would be MOST helpful to scientists trying to identify this insect?   S7L1b

A. microscope

B. binoculars

C. dichotomous key

D. Petri dish

20. In a deciduous forest in autumn, broad-leaf trees shed their leaves to prepare for winter. Before losing their leaves, the leaves turn colors created by pigments within the leaf. What type of cell organelle is responsible for the color of leaves in the fall?   S7L2b

A. mitochondria   C. plastid

B. ribosome   D. flagellum

Please go on to the next page

Use the information below to answer questions 21 and 22.

A newly discovered type of grass looks blue-green from far away. However, when scientists examined the grass up close they noticed individual blue and green cells.

21. What is the most likely inheritance pattern for color in this grass species? S7L3a

    A. co-dominance

    B. incomplete dominance

    C. dominant/recessive

    D. polygenic

22. Which tool would be most helpful to observe the cellular structure of this new type of grass? S7CS4b

    A. microscope

    B. binoculars

    C. magnifying glass

    D. Petri dish

23. Which two organisms you have studied are commonly used as examples to demonstrate the process of evolution? S7L5a

    A. Galapagos finches and peppered moths

    B. strangler figs and sloths

    C. lions and leopards

    D. lunar moths and goldfinches

24. What type of living thing can reproduce sexually using flowers, seeds and fruits? S7L3b

    A. animals

    B. fungi

    C. plants

    D. bacteria

25. While working in the lab, a student accidentally breaks the knob on a microscope. What should the student do next? S7CS2a/S7CS2c

    A. put the knob back on the microscope

    B. exchange the microscope for an unbroken one

    C. immediately tell the teacher

    D. tell other students and ask their advice

26. A scientific researcher was interested in determining the length of time it took to domesticate an animal. He kept and bred over 300 wild silver foxes. He would select the tamest puppy from each litter to breed with another hand-picked tame puppy. This type of breeding is called S7L3c

    A. cloning.

    B. genetic engineering.

    C. interbreeding.

    D. selective breeding.

27. Which one of the following organisms would most likely be considered prey? S7L4a

    A. grizzly bear

    B. rabbit

    C. wolf

    D. human

28. What unit is the BEST to use when measuring the length of rose flower pedals? S7CS3a/S7CS3c

    A. micrometer (0.000001 m)

    B. centimeter (0.01 m)

    C. meter (1 m)

    D. kilometer (1,000 m)

Please go on to the next page

Use the information and the table below to answer question 29.

Some trees, like the tulip poplar (*Liriodendron tulipifera*) or ginkgo (*Ginkgo biloba*), turn a vivid yellow in autumn.

Pigment type	Color	Examples
xanthophyll	yellow	bananas
anthocyanin	red or purple	apples and blueberries
tannin	brown	coffee, tea and coco
chlorophyll	green	grasses and pine trees
carotenes	orange	carrots

29. What type of pigment is responsible   S7CS6c
for this yellow color?

A. xanthophyll   C. tannin

B. anthocyanin   D. carotenes

30. Which experiment would be   S7CS7c/S7CS9c
the BEST to determine if the
amount of food affects the breeding rate of
fruit flies?

A. Put one covered test tube of fruit flies
near a heater, and the other in the
refrigerator both with 5 grams of food.

B. Put one covered test tube of fruit flies in a
dark drawer with 5 grams of food, and
one on a sunny windowsill with 2.5
grams of food.

C. Put one covered test tube of fruit flies
near a heater with 5 grams of food, and
another test tube in the refrigerator with
2.5 grams of food.

D. Keep both test tubes side by side with the
same amount of light and at the same
temperature, but give one 5 grams of
food and the other 2.5 grams of food.

Please STOP!

Do not go on to the next page!

Section 2

31. In a particular biome, rainfall is medium and summer temperatures average about 12°C (54°F). This is a description of this biome's _____ factors.   S7L4e

    A. biotic

    B. abiotic

    C. biotic and abiotic

    D. population

32. How do producers get energy?   S7L4a

    A. They get it from the biotic factors in an ecosystem.

    B. They get it from abiotic factors in the ecosystem.

    C. They get it from the decomposing organisms.

    D. They get it from humans.

33. Which food would have the most concentrated source of energy for a human?   S7L4b

    A. salmon   C. broccoli

    B. chicken   D. hamburger

Use the information below to answer questions 34 – 36.

In a ten-square mile portion of a state park, there are approximately 500 raccoons and 100 coyotes.

34. Which population is denser?   S7L4c

    A. the raccoon population

    B. the coyote population

    C. neither, they are of equal density

    D. cannot assess without knowing the growth rate.

35. Several animals within the state park have become infected with an airborne viral illness. Which animal stands a greater chance of contracting this disease?   S7L4c

    A. the raccoon

    B. the coyote

    C. They are equally at risk.

    D. Neither are at risk, since animals do not contract viruses.

36. Humans begin drilling for oil within the state park. Which population will be impacted the most?   S7L4c

    A. the tree population

    B. the raccoon population

    C. the coyote population

    D. they will be equally impacted by the drilling

37. Beavers use trees to build dams and create nesting lodges. The beavers strip the leaves off the branches of the tree for food. How would you classify this type of relationship?   S7L4d

    A. commensalistic   C. predatory

    B. competitive   D. symbiotic

Please go on to the next page

38. A meerkat (*Suricata suricatta*) is a type of mongoose that lives in burrows in the African desert. The meerkat mainly eats small invertebrates, snakes, lizards, plants, eggs and other small mammals found above ground and in their burrows. What is this a description of?   S7L4e

    A. an ecosystem   C. a species

    B. a community   D. a niche

39. In a bacterial colony, 1% of the individual bacteria randomly produce a chemical that protects the bacteria from harmful substances used by humans. This adaptation changes the DNA of the bacterial colony. What is this random change in the DNA code called?   S7L5b

    A. mutation

    B. gene flow

    C. genetic marker

    D. bottlenecking

40. A child takes a trip with her family to a nearby town. Along the way, the family passes many lakes, several bogs, grasses, moss, lichens, caribou, birds and insects. What biome does this family most likely live in?   S7L4e

    A. tundra

    B. deciduous forest

    C. grassland

    D. rainforest

41. Use the cladogram below to select the two most distantly related organisms.   S7L5a

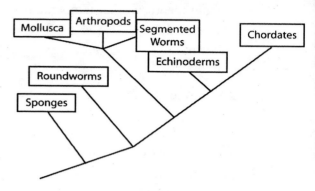

    A. sponges and chordates

    B. echinoderms and sponges

    C. arthropods and segmented worms

    D. roundworms and echinoderms

42. In central America, a plant called Bullhorn Acacia (*Acacia cornigera*) has a relationship with stinging ants (*Pseudomyrmex ferruginea*). The plant has specialized hollow thorns that provide shelter for the ants. The ants, in turn, bite or sting any living thing that comes into contact with the plant. What type of species interaction is occurring between the plants and the ants?   S7L4d

    A. commensalism   C. predator/prey

    B. mutualism   D. parasitism

43. What is the process of grouping similar things together called?   S7L1a

    A. dichotomous key

    B. taxonologist

    C. classifying

    D. none of the above

Please go on to the next page

44. On the Galapagos Islands many different species of iguana exist. Some iguanas are large, black and eat food found in the ocean. Other iguanas are smaller, different colored and eat food found on the island. What process MOST likely explains the differences seen in the iguana species? **S7L5b**

   A. convergent evolution

   B. bottleneck

   C. natural selection

   D. artificial selection

45. Which example is the most specific grouping of living things? **S7L1b**

   A. Animalia

   B. Insecta

   C. Formicidae

   D. *Aenictogiton sulcatus*

46. Use the image to determine which fossil is the oldest. **S7L5c**

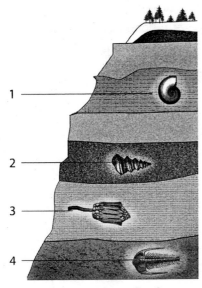

   A. 1   C. 3

   B. 2   D. 4

47. If air pollution got really bad and blocked out all sunlight, what would eventually happen to organisms? **S7L4b**

   A. Plants would die but animals would survive by eating only other animals.

   B. Plants would survive on inorganic chemicals but animals would die.

   C. Plants and animals would survive without changing.

   D. Both plants and animals would die.

48. What type of rock can contain fossils? **S7L5c**

   A. Solidified lava from a volcanic eruption.

   B. Rock formed from the shifting tectonic plates.

   C. Rock formed from the deposits of a flood.

   D. Rock formed from an undersea thermal vent.

49. Which example below is the simplest component of a multicellular organism? **S7L2c**

   A. large intestine

   B. skull

   C. lymphatic system

   D. red blood cell

50. Which one of the following organisms would be considered prey? **S7L4a**

   A. grass   C. chipmunk

   B. rabbit   D. all of the above

Please go on to the next page

51. Which organism would be found at the top of an energy pyramid? S7L4b

    A. moth   C. minnow
    B. shark   D. crayfish

52. Why do cells in a multicellular organism have different shapes? S7L2c

    A. because the shape helps each cell to carry out its specialized function

    B. because the long fingerlike extensions help transmit information through the body

    C. because each cell is different and unique

    D. cells in a multicellular organism do not have different shapes

53. Which questions would be LEAST useful when developing a dichotomous key about hats? S7L1a

    A. What type of material is the hat made out of?

    B. Does the hat have a visor or bill?

    C. Is the hat held onto the head with a strap?

    D. Is the hat worn on the head?

54. A random variation in the coloration of peppered moths allowed the species to survive under changed environmental conditions. What caused the random variation in the moth population? S7L5b

    A. genes flowing

    B. founder effect

    C. convergent evolution

    D. mutation

55. If a dog skin cell was placed in a hypotonic solution and left overnight, what would most likely happen to the skin cell? S7L2a

    A. nothing

    B. it would swell and burst

    C. it would shrivel and die

    D. first it would swell, then maintain that size

56. What is one main difference between respiration and photosynthesis? S7L2d

    A. Photosynthesis makes energy and respiration destroys energy.

    B. Photosynthesis stores energy and respiration breaks down energy.

    C. Photosynthesis takes place in plant cells only and respiration takes place in animal cells only.

    D. Photosynthesis uses inorganic chemicals to make energy and respiration does not.

57. What are the only type of organisms that can carry out chemosynthesis? S7L2d

    A. animals   C. fungi
    B. plants   D. bacteria

Please go on to the next page

58. According to Darwin, natural   S7L5b
    selection produces the best-suited
    organisms in an environment because

    A. the organisms with the most adaptive
        traits produce many offspring.

    B. The strong protect the weak.

    C. gene flow is the only way species can
        change over time.

    D. bottlenecks are good for populations to
        eliminate the weak.

59. Where does the energy you need to   S7L4b
    live ultimately come from?

    A. bacteria

    B. the Sun

    C. meat only

    D. plants only

60. If a cell has a flagellum on its   S7L2b
    surface, it is most likely

    A. an animal cell.

    B. a plant cell.

    C. a hypotonic cell.

    D. a diseased cell.

Please STOP!

**Do not go on
to the next page!**

Georgia 7th Grade CRCT
Post Test 2

Post Test 2   **Answer Sheet**

Name: _____

Section 1

1. Ⓐ Ⓑ Ⓒ Ⓓ
2. Ⓐ Ⓑ Ⓒ Ⓓ
3. Ⓐ Ⓑ Ⓒ Ⓓ
4. Ⓐ Ⓑ Ⓒ Ⓓ
5. Ⓐ Ⓑ Ⓒ Ⓓ
6. Ⓐ Ⓑ Ⓒ Ⓓ
7. Ⓐ Ⓑ Ⓒ Ⓓ
8. Ⓐ Ⓑ Ⓒ Ⓓ
9. Ⓐ Ⓑ Ⓒ Ⓓ
10. Ⓐ Ⓑ Ⓒ Ⓓ
11. Ⓐ Ⓑ Ⓒ Ⓓ
12. Ⓐ Ⓑ Ⓒ Ⓓ
13. Ⓐ Ⓑ Ⓒ Ⓓ
14. Ⓐ Ⓑ Ⓒ Ⓓ
15. Ⓐ Ⓑ Ⓒ Ⓓ
16. Ⓐ Ⓑ Ⓒ Ⓓ
17. Ⓐ Ⓑ Ⓒ Ⓓ
18. Ⓐ Ⓑ Ⓒ Ⓓ
19. Ⓐ Ⓑ Ⓒ Ⓓ
20. Ⓐ Ⓑ Ⓒ Ⓓ
21. Ⓐ Ⓑ Ⓒ Ⓓ

22. Ⓐ Ⓑ Ⓒ Ⓓ
23. Ⓐ Ⓑ Ⓒ Ⓓ
24. Ⓐ Ⓑ Ⓒ Ⓓ
25. Ⓐ Ⓑ Ⓒ Ⓓ
26. Ⓐ Ⓑ Ⓒ Ⓓ
27. Ⓐ Ⓑ Ⓒ Ⓓ
28. Ⓐ Ⓑ Ⓒ Ⓓ
29. Ⓐ Ⓑ Ⓒ Ⓓ
30. Ⓐ Ⓑ Ⓒ Ⓓ

Section 2

31. Ⓐ Ⓑ Ⓒ Ⓓ
32. Ⓐ Ⓑ Ⓒ Ⓓ
33. Ⓐ Ⓑ Ⓒ Ⓓ
34. Ⓐ Ⓑ Ⓒ Ⓓ
35. Ⓐ Ⓑ Ⓒ Ⓓ
36. Ⓐ Ⓑ Ⓒ Ⓓ
37. Ⓐ Ⓑ Ⓒ Ⓓ
38. Ⓐ Ⓑ Ⓒ Ⓓ
39. Ⓐ Ⓑ Ⓒ Ⓓ
40. Ⓐ Ⓑ Ⓒ Ⓓ

41. Ⓐ Ⓑ Ⓒ Ⓓ
42. Ⓐ Ⓑ Ⓒ Ⓓ
43. Ⓐ Ⓑ Ⓒ Ⓓ
44. Ⓐ Ⓑ Ⓒ Ⓓ
45. Ⓐ Ⓑ Ⓒ Ⓓ
46. Ⓐ Ⓑ Ⓒ Ⓓ
47. Ⓐ Ⓑ Ⓒ Ⓓ
48. Ⓐ Ⓑ Ⓒ Ⓓ
49. Ⓐ Ⓑ Ⓒ Ⓓ
50. Ⓐ Ⓑ Ⓒ Ⓓ
51. Ⓐ Ⓑ Ⓒ Ⓓ
52. Ⓐ Ⓑ Ⓒ Ⓓ
53. Ⓐ Ⓑ Ⓒ Ⓓ
54. Ⓐ Ⓑ Ⓒ Ⓓ
55. Ⓐ Ⓑ Ⓒ Ⓓ
56. Ⓐ Ⓑ Ⓒ Ⓓ
57. Ⓐ Ⓑ Ⓒ Ⓓ
58. Ⓐ Ⓑ Ⓒ Ⓓ
59. Ⓐ Ⓑ Ⓒ Ⓓ
60. Ⓐ Ⓑ Ⓒ Ⓓ

Session 1

1. When making a dichotomous key, what is the first step?   S7L1a

    A. use the specific characteristics to narrow down the smaller groups into specific objects

    B. use the general characteristics to divide the large group into smaller groups

    C. select between pairs of choices

    D. group different things together

2. What is the main purpose of the excretory system?   S7L2e

    A. to remove wastes

    B. to transport nutrients

    C. to move the body

    D. to respond to stimuli

3. The marine iguana (*Amblyrhynchus cristatus*) found on the Galapagos Islands specializes in eating marine alga found under water. The iguana has special adaptations that expel excess salt through its nose. Over millions of years, what do you expect would be another LIKLEY adaptation of the marine iguana population?   S7L5b

    A. the development of webbed feet

    B. the development of wings

    C. the development of large eyes

    D. the development of longer legs

4. Which example is the most general grouping of living things?   S7L1b

    A. Plantae

    B. Magnoliopsida

    C. Ranunculaceae

    D. *Hepatica americana*

5. A volcano erupts on an island in the South Pacific. The eruption of this volcano threatens   S7L4c

    A. only large, dense populations.

    B. only small, sparse populations.

    C. all populations equally.

    D. no populations on the island.

6. Which example below is the most complex component of a multicellular organism?   S7L2c

    A. heart

    B. brain

    C. skin cell

    D. reproductive system

7. What type of organism is LEAST likely to become a fossil?   S7L5c

    A. a single celled euglena

    B. a whale

    C. a crocodile

    D. a clam

8. If the F_1 generation shows a phenotype that is completely different from the P generation, and is most easily described as a blending of both the parents, then the inheritance pattern is most likely   S7L3a

    A. co-dominance.

    B. incomplete dominance.

    C. dominant/recessive.

    D. polygenic.

Please go on to the next page

9. Why is inbreeding bad for organisms?   S7L3c

   A. Inbreeding can amplify genetic or physical problems.

   B. Inbreeding reduces genetic diversity among animals.

   C. both A and B

   D. none of the above

10. Which one of the following organisms would be considered a predator?   S7L4a

    A. sea grass

    B. honeysuckle vine

    C. sugar maple tree

    D. raccoon

11. Which type of food product depends on anaerobic respiration during production?   S7L2d

    A. corn on the cob

    B. bread

    C. cola

    D. tomatoes

12. Which one of the following organisms is a carnivore?   S7L4a

    A. snake
    B. human
    C. shrub
    D. caterpillar

13. What type of living thing reproduces using binary fission or budding?   S7L3b

    A. animals
    B. fungi
    C. plants
    D. bacteria

14. What type of food would have the least concentrated energy for a human?   S7L4b

    A. corn
    B. bread
    C. peanuts
    D. chicken

15. For thousands of years humans have preserved meat by applying a hypertonic salt mixture directly to the surface of the meat tissue. How does this process help to preserve the meat?   S7L2a

    A. The salt mixture draws the water out of the muscle cells and dries the meat.

    B. The salt mixture encourages water to flow into the muscle cells and dries the meat.

    C. The salt mixture encourages water to flow into the muscle cells and soaks the meat.

    D. Salting meat does not preserve it.

16. How do animals lose energy to the environment?   S7L4b

    A. Animals lose energy to the environment by eating other organisms.

    B. Animals lose energy to the environment by living as a colony with other organisms.

    C. Animals lose energy to the environment as body heat.

    D. Animals lose energy to the environment by growing larger.

Please go on to the next page

17. What aspect of the Galapagos finch's niche caused a change in their physical characteristics? S7L5a

    A. habitat

    B. exercise

    C. diet

    D. predatory controls

18. Which graph below shows the carrying capacity for an organism? S7L4c

    A.
    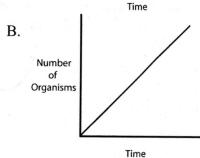
    Number of Organisms

    Time

    B.
    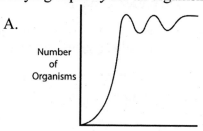
    Number of Organisms

    Time

    C.
    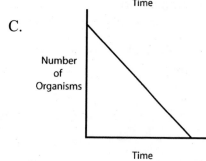
    Number of Organisms

    Time

    D.
    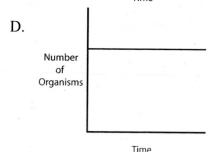
    Number of Organisms

    Time

19. A spider monkey (*Ateles marginatus*) S7L4d is a fruit-eating monkey found in the rainforest. The monkey eats fruits produced by the strangler fig (*Ficus citrifolia*). The monkey eats the fruit and the seeds of the fig. Later, the seeds are excreted by the monkey, and deposited elsewhere in the rainforest. The monkey gets food and the vine gets its seeds dispersed throughout the rainforest. What type of organism relationship is this?

    A. competitive

    B. mutualistic

    C. predatory

    D. commensalistic

20. Large herding animals, like zebras, S7L5b have an increased flight response. This means that the animal runs away at the slightest sign of danger. How has this behavioral adaptation helped the zebra?

    A. It has helped the zebra to avoid predators faster.

    B. It has helped the zebra develop long, thin legs.

    C. It has helped the zebra develop large ears.

    D. It has helped the zebra to develop stripes.

21. The Bald Eagle (*Haliaeetus leucocephalus*) captures and eats salmon (*Oncorhynchus tshawytscha*). What type of organism relationship does the eagle have with the salmon? S7L4d

    A. mutualistic

    B. predatory

    C. commensalistic

    D. symbiotic

Please go on to the next page

22. When studying biomes, it is important to remember   S7L4e

   A. that one biome quickly changes into the next.

   B. that one biome gradually merges into the next.

   C. that biomes are classified by rare specialized species found only in that land area.

   D. biomes only describe animal life found in a particular area.

Use the table to answer question 23.

Number of months	Number of wild hogs
4	5
8	50
12	500
16	?

23. At 16 months, approximately how many wild hogs will MOST likely live in this area?   S7CS6b/S7CS6c

   A. 500   C. 50,000

   B. 5,000   D. 500,000

24. According to the graph, as the concentration of copper increases, the number of duckweed plants   S7CS6b/S7CS6c

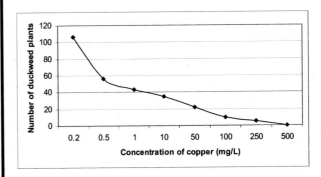

   A. increases.

   B. decreases.

   C. stays the same.

   D. increases then stays the same.

25. A particular biome is dominated by broadleaf trees that change color in autumn. What biome is this?   S7L4e

   A. tundra

   B. deciduous forest

   C. grassland

   D. rainforest

Use the cladogram below to answer question 26.

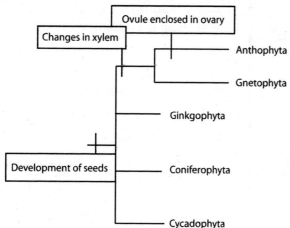

26. What trait separates anthophyta from gnetophyta?   S7L5a

    A. development of seeds

    B. changes in xylem

    C. ovule enclosed in an ovary

    D. cannot determine the answer from the information provided

27. Which event will MOST likely lead to the formation of fossils?   S7L5c

    A. the death of a zebra on the African plain

    B. the burning of wood in a home

    C. a massive mudslide

    D. the death of a beached whale

28. What type of organism interaction is shown in the picture?   S7L4d

    A. mutualism

    B. commensalism

    C. parasitism

    D. predator/prey

29. How are photosynthesis and respiration similar?   S7L2d

    A. They both take place inside cells.

    B. They both make energy.

    C. They both break down glucose.

    D. They both remove cellular wastes.

30. Two naturalists were overseeing a wildlife study on Atlantic Ridley sea turtles (*Lepidochelys kempii*). Which of the following is an observation?   S7CS9a/S7CS9b

    A. "I believe female sea turtles dig nests in the sand."

    B. "How do female sea turtles dig nests in the sand?"

    C. "A female sea turtle took 24 minutes to dig a nest in the sand."

    D. "I would like to see when female sea turtles dig their nests in the sand."

Please STOP!
Do not go on to the next page!

31. This piece of lab equipment is used to S7CS4b

A. measure temperature.

B. culture bacteria.

C. view distant objects.

D. view small objects.

32. Which question would be MOST useful when developing a dichotomous key about the two butterflies seen below? S7L1a

A. Does the butterfly eat nectar?

B. Is the butterfly mostly dark in color?

C. Does the butterfly have wings?

D. Is the butterfly mostly active during the day?

33. What are the main types of muscular tissue? S7L2e

A. veins, arteries and heart

B. kidneys, bladder and urethra

C. skeletal, cardiac and smooth

D. lungs and diaphragm

34. A particular type of organism reproduces using spores and obtains nutrients from other dead organisms. To which kingdom does this organism belong? S7L1b

A. Fungi

B. Plantae

C. Animalia

D. None of the above

35. A section of creek has several plants and animals living in close proximity. What is this an example of? S7L4e

A. biome

B. community

C. species

D. niche

36. A yellow flower is crossed with a blue flower. The resulting F_1 flowers are all green. What is the inheritance pattern for flower color in this example? S7L3a

A. co-dominance

B. incomplete dominance

C. dominant/recessive

D. polygenic

37. Why is cell division necessary for organisms? S7L3b

A. cell division replaces old cells and allows the organism to grow and reproduce

B. cell division is not necessary for organisms

C. cell division is only necessary for diseased or stressed organisms

D. cell division only occurs in somatic cells of an organism

Please go on to the next page

38. Which one of the following organisms is an omnivore?   S7L4a

   A. wolf   C. horse

   B. raccoon   D. snake

39. Mendel practiced selective breeding with pea plants to better study their characteristics. What does the term "selective breeding" refer to?   S7L3c

   A. only allowing plants with certain characteristics to breed

   B. allowing plants with any characteristic to naturally pollinate

   C. selecting only the best co-workers to help him with his experiment

   D. the natural breeding of pea plants

40. When new grass grows from the ground, where does the matter that makes up the plant tissue come from?   S7L4a

   A. It is created by the seed.

   B. It is created by the endosperm.

   C. It is recycled from the death and decay of other organisms.

   D. It is created from the death and decay of other organisms.

41. If an animal dies and contains 12 grams of a radioactive isotope, how much of the parent isotope will remain after one half-life?   S7L5c

   A. 6 grams   C. 3 grams

   B. ½ gram   D. 2 grams

42. What type of organism consumes the least concentrated energy source?   S7L4b

   A. producer

   B. primary consumer

   C. secondary consumer

   D. top consumer

43. A component of the human body is made up of organs like the diaphragm and lungs. This component performs a particular function for humans. Which example below correctly identifies the complexity of this component?   S7L2c

   A. cell   C. organ

   B. tissue   D. organ system

44. The number of individuals a given environment can support is called the   S7L4c

   A. carrying capacity.

   B. limiting factor.

   C. density dependent.

   D. density independent.

45. If a cow liver cell was placed in a hypertonic solution and left overnight, what would most likely happen to the liver cell?   S7L2a

   A. nothing

   B. it would swell and burst

   C. it would shrivel and die

   D. first it would swell then it would remain the same size

Please go on to the next page

46. What aspect of the peppered moth's niche caused a change in their physical characteristics?   S7L5a

    A. habitat

    B. exercise

    C. diet

    D. primary controls

47. Which graph below shows a positive growth rate for a population?   S7L4c

    A.
    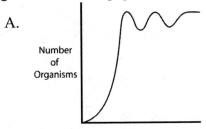

    B.
    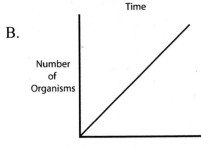

    C.
    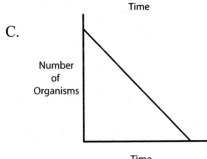

    D.
    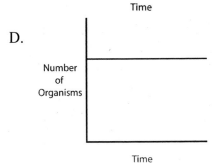

48. *Necator americanus* enters the human body from the soil through the foot. *N. americanus* then migrates throughout the body, eventually arriving in the small intestine where it absorbs food from the human. *N. americanus* receives a place to live and food from the human, and the human is harmed. What type of organism relationship is this?   S7L4d

    A. commensalism

    B. mutualism

    C. predator/prey

    D. parasitism

49. Prey animals, like deer or horses, have eyes located on the side of their head. This helps the animal see in almost every direction. How has this adaptation helped prey animals?   S7L5b

    A. It helps the animal avoid predators.

    B. It helps the animal locate all food sources.

    C. It helps the animal herd together.

    D. It helps the animal smell everything in the environment.

50. Some ferns and orchids are epiphytic and grow on top of pre-existing trees. Having a **few** epiphytic plants grow on their branches neither helps nor harms the tree. The epiphytic plants receive more light in the tree top then they would on the ground. What type of organism relationship does the tree have with epiphytic plants?   S7L4d

    A. mutualistic

    B. predatory

    C. commensalistic

    D. symbiotic

51. What cell parts are found in plant   S7L2b
cells but not in animal cells?

    A. nucleus and vacuoles

    B. cell wall and plastid

    C. cilia and flagella

    D. mitochondria and cell membrane

52. Which grouping example below   S7L1b
includes the fewest number of
organisms?

    A. Kingdom Animalia

    B. Class Insecta

    C. Order Mantodea

    D. Family Mantidae

53. In this biome, average summer   S7L4e
temperature is around 30°C. Cacti,
grass, insects and lizards can be found there.
This is a description of this biome's
_____ factors.

    A. biotic

    B. abiotic

    C. biotic and abiotic

    D. population

54. What type of organism is usually   S7L4b
found at the top of an energy
pyramid?

    A. saprophyte

    B. carnivore

    C. herbivore

    D. producer

55. The marsupial Tasmanian devil and   S7L5b
the mammalian dingo look very
similar but did not develop from a common
ancestor. Which evolutionary idea best
explains this similarity?

Tasmanian Devil

Dingo

    A. genetic drift

    B. divergent evolution

    C. adaptive radiation

    D. convergent evolution

Please go on to the next page

56. A mother has the genotype $I^A I^A$ for blood type. A father that has the genotype $I^B I^B$ for blood type. Their child has a genotype $I^A I^B$ for blood type, giving the phenotype AB for blood. What is the inheritance pattern for blood type? S7L3a

A. co-dominance

B. incomplete dominance

C. dominant/recessive

D. polygenic

57. An animal dies and contains 6 grams of a radioactive isotope. After two half-lives, how much of the parent isotope will remain? S7L5c

A. ½ of the initial amount

B. 1.5 grams

C. 3 grams

D. 1/16th of the initial amount

58. What is an estuary? S7L4e

A. a freshwater ecosystem

B. a terrestrial ecosystem

C. an area where fresh water meets salt water

D. a type of plant found in the rainforest

59. The brain is the to human as the _____ is to the eukaryotic cell. S7L2b

A. cytoplasm

B. mitochondria

C. ribosome

D. nucleus

Use the cladogram below to answer the following question.

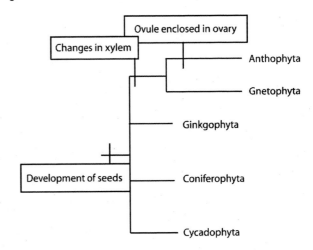

60. What trait separates the plants shown from all other plants? S7L5a

A. development of seeds

B. changes in xylem

C. ovule enclosed in an ovary

D. cannot determine the answer from the information provided

Please STOP!

Do not go on to the next page!

Appendix A
Concept Maps

Concept maps are an important tool used in science, social studies and math. A **concept map** is a graphical way to show information. A concept map can be in a structured outline form (hierarchy form), where the main topic is placed at the top of the page and the supporting ideas are underneath. A concept map can also be in a spider-web form, where the central idea is placed in the center of the page and supporting ideas radiate outward like spokes on a wheel. Each idea is connected to the main topic with lines or words.

Concept maps can be used to recall prior knowledge, before beginning a domain or chapter, to help you review what you may already know about the subject. Later, after completing the domain or chapter, you can return to your concept map and change it based on new information you may have learned during the section.

When developing a concept map, the first question you should ask is "What is the main idea?" You should decide the main word, topic or problem to use to build the map. The main idea will be related to all other topics within the map. The next steps involve brainstorming other topics related to the main idea.

Let's build a concept map about a familiar idea, food. The first step is to quickly write down ten or more things/concepts about food. The second step is to rank the things/concepts you brainstormed from the most general to the most specific. Use the space below to begin building your concept map.

If you need further help, use the following steps to help you get started. Write the word "Food" at the top of your page. Next, list the most general concepts directly under the word "Food" (in this example, it was categories of food, like meat or fruits). Lastly, more specific ideas are located near the bottom of the page (here it was specific types of food and their nutrient content). Look at the sample map about food shown below:

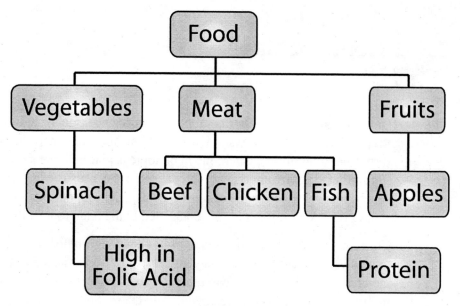

This hierarchical form may look different than the one you have created. That is fine. The important thing to remember is to **correctly describe the relationships** between the categories you define.

When making a concept map, it is important to use a *pencil*, and remember that mistakes are *okay*. A concept map is a helpful tool for you, the student, to use to organize and remember important ideas and concepts. You may re-draw or re-work your map several times before you decide on the final structure.

Review the sample concept maps below:

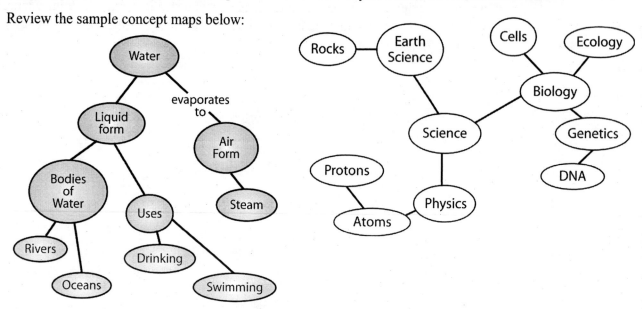

Now it is your turn: develop a concept map about clothing, a sport or a hobby.

U

unicellular 33
urinary tract 45

V

vacuole 31

Z

zone
  types of 85
zygote 47

PASSING THE
GEORGIA 7TH GRADE CRCT
IN SCIENCE
ANSWER KEY

2007
Written to the GPS 2006 Standards

Michelle Gunter

American Book Company
PO Box 2638
Woodstock, GA 30188-1383
Toll Free: 1 (888) 264-5877   Phone: (770) 928-2834
Fax: (770) 928-7483 Toll Free Fax 1 (866) 827-3240
Web Site: www.americanbookcompany.com

Georgia 7th Grade CRCT Test in Science
Chart of Standards

Passing the Georgia 7th Grade CRCT Test in Science	

Chart of Standards

The following chart correlates each question on the Diagnostic Test, Practice Test 1, and Practice Test 2 to the Science *GPS Standards published by the Georgia Department of Education*. These test questions are also correlated with chapters in the *7th Grade CRCT Test in Science.*

Competency Standards	Chapter Number	Diagnostic Test Questions	Practice Test 1 Questions	Practice Test 2 Questions
S7L1 Students will investigate the diversity of living organisms and how they can be compared scientifically.				
a. Demonstrate the process for the development of a dichotomous key.	1	7, 31	43, 53	1, 32
b. Classify organisms based on a six-kingdom system and a dichotomous key.	2	34, 36, 44	19, 45	4, 34, 52

Competency Standards	Chapter Number	Diagnostic Test Questions	Practice Test 1 Questions	Practice Test 2 Questions
S7L2 Students will describe the structure and function of cells, tissues, organs, and organ systems.				
a. Explain that cells take in nutrients in order to grow and divide and to make needed materials.	3	14, 35	1, 11, 55	15, 45
b. Relate cell structures (cell membrane, nucleus, cytoplasm, chloroplasts, mitochondria) to basic cell functions.	4	8, 22, 46	20, 60	51, 59
c. Explain that cells are organized into tissues, tissues into organs, organs into systems, and systems into organisms.	5	13, 42	49, 52	6, 43
d. Explain that tissues, organs, and organ systems serve the needs cell have for oxygen, food, and waste removal.	6	10, 27	56, 57	11, 29
e. Explain the role of the major organ systems in the human body.	7	15, 38	3, 16	2, 33

Competency Standards	Chapter Number	Diagnostic Test Questions	Practice Test 1 Questions	Practice Test 2 Questions
S7L3 Students will recognize how biological traits are passed on to successive generations.				
a. Explain the role of genes and chromosomes in the process of inheriting a specific trait.	8	11, 37	4, 21	8, 36, 56
b. Compare and contrast sexual and asexual reproduction in organisms (bacteria, protists, fungi, plants and animals).	9	4, 48	13, 24	13, 37
c. Recognize that selective breeding can produce plants and animals with desired traits.	10	12, 40	6, 26	9, 39

Competency Standards	Chapter Number	Diagnostic Test Questions	Practice Test 1 Questions	Practice Test 2 Questions
S7L4 Students will examine the dependence of organisms on one another and their environments.				
a. Demonstrate in a food web that matter is transferred from on organism to another and can recycle between organisms and their environments.	11	16, 17, 39, 41	5, 27, 32, 50	10, 12, 38, 40
b. Explain in a food web that sunlight is the source of energy and that this energy moves from organism to organism.	12	18, 19, 43, 53	33, 47, 51, 59	14, 16, 31, 42, 54
c. Recognize that changes in environmental conditions can affect the survival of both individuals and entire species.	13	9, 20, 58, 60	7, 9, 34, 35, 36	5, 18, 44, 47
d. categorize relationships between organisms that are competitive or mutually beneficial.	14	21, 33, 45, 50, 51	10, 12, 31, 37, 42	19, 21, 28, 48, 50
e. Describe the characteristics of Earth's major terrestrial biomes (i.e., tropical rain forest, savannah, temperate, desert, taiga, tundra, and mountain) and aquatic communities (i.e., freshwater, estuaries, and marine).	15	23, 25, 30, 52, 55	14, 38, 40	22, 25, 35, 53, 58

Competency Standards	Chapter Number	Diagnostic Test Questions	Practice Test 1 Questions	Practice Test 2 Questions
S7L5 Students will examine the evolution of living organisms through inherited characteristics that promote the survival or organisms and the survival of successive generations of their offspring.				
a. Explain how physical characteristics of organisms have changed over successive generations. (i.e., Darwin's finches and the peppered moths of Manchester).	16	26, 28, 49, 54	8, 15, 23, 41	17, 26, 46, 60
b. Describe ways in which species on earth have evolved due to natural selection.	17	24, 32, 56, 57	17, 39, 44, 54, 58	3, 20, 49, 55
c. Explain how the fossil record found in sedimentary rock provides evidence for the long history of changing life forms.	18	29, 47, 59	18, 46, 48	7, 27, 41, 57

Competency Standards	Chapter Number	Diagnostic Test Questions	Practice Test 1 Questions	Practice Test 2 Questions
S7CS2 Students will use standard safety practices for all classroom laboratory and field investigations.				
a. Follow correct procedures for use of scientific apparatus.		1	25	
c. Follow correct protocol for identifying and reporting safely problems and violations.		1	25	
S7CS3 Students will have the computation and estimation skills necessary for analyzing data and following scientific explanations.				
a. Analyze scientific data by using, interpreting and comparing numbers in several equivalent forms, such as integers, fractions, decimals and percents.			28	
c. Apply the metric system to a scientific investigation that includes metric to metric conversion. (i.e. centimeters to meters)			28	
S7CS4 Students will use tools and instruments for observing, measuring and manipulating equipment and materials in scientific activities.				
b. Use appropriate tools for measuring objects and/or substances.		6	22	

Competency Standards	Chapter Number	Diagnostic Test Questions	Practice Test 1 Questions	Practice Test 2 Questions
S7CS6 Students will question scientific claims and arguments effectively.				
a. Write clear, step-by-step instructions for conducting particular scientific investigations, operating a piece of equipment or following a procedure.				
b. Write for scientific purposes incorporating data from circle, bar and line graphs, two-way data tables, diagrams and symbols.				23, 24
c. Organize scientific information using appropriate simple tables, charts and graphs, and identify relationships they reveal.		2	29	23, 24
S7CS7 Students will question scientific claims and arguments effectively.				
c. Questions the value of arguments based on small samples of data, biased samples or samples for which there was no control.			30	

Competency Standards	Chapter Number	Diagnostic Test Questions	Practice Test 1 Questions	Practice Test 2 Questions
S7CS9 Students will investigate the features of the process of scientific inquiry.				
a. Investigations are conducted for different reasons, which include exploring new phenomena, confirming previous results, testing how well a theory predicts, and comparing competing theories.				30
b. Scientific investigations usually involve collecting evidence, reasoning, devising hypotheses, and formulating explanations to make sense of collected evidence.		3, 5	2	30
c. Scientific experiments investigate the effect of one variable on another. All other variables are kept constant.			30	

ANSWER KEY

Diagnostic Test
Pages 1 – 12

1. A	11. A	21. A	31. D	41. C	51. B
2. A	12. D	22. A	32. B	42. D	52. B
3. B	13. B	23. B	33. B	43. D	53. D
4. C	14. C	24. A	34. B	44. B	54. B
5. D	15. B	25. D	35. D	45. B	55. C
6. C	16. A	26. B	36. B	46. A	56. D
7. A	17. B	27. A	37. A	47. A	57. B
8. A	18. D	28. D	38. B	48. A	58. A
9. B	19. B	29. A	39. C	49. D	59. B
10. D	20. B	30. D	40. D	50. C	60. B

CHAPTER 1 MAKING AND USING A DICHOTOMOUS KEY

Chapter 1 Review

Page 18

1. C 2. B 3. D 4. B 5. C

CHAPTER 2 SIX KINGDOMS - TAXONOMY

Chapter 2 Review

Page 22

1. C 2. B 3. C 4. A 5. B

CHAPTER 3 CELLS AND CELLULAR TRANSPORT

Chapter 3 Review

Page 28

1. D 2. B 3. B 4. A 5. C

CHAPTER 4 CELLULAR PARTS

Chapter 4 Review

Page 32

1. D 2. A 3. D 4. B 5. A

CHAPTER 5 CELLULAR HIERARCHY

Chapter 5 Review

Page 36

1. B   2. B   3. A   4. C   5. D

CHAPTER 6 CELLULAR NEEDS

Chapter 6 Review

Page 40

1. C   2. D   3. C   4. B   5. A

CHAPTER 7 THE HUMAN BODY

Chapter 7 Review

Page 46

1. D   2. B   3. A   4. C   5. B

CHAPTER 8 GENETICS AND CHROMOSOMES

Chapter 8 Review

Page 50

1. C   2. A   3. C   4. C   5. A

CHAPTER 9 SEXUAL AND ASEXUAL REPRODUCTION

Chapter 9 Review

Page 54

1. C   2. A   3. A   4. B   5. A

CHAPTER 10 GETTING DESIRED TRAITS

Chapter 10 Review

Page 58

1. C   2. A   3. B   4. D   5. D

DOMAIN 1 REVIEW

Pages 59 – 62

1. B	6. B	11. A	16. D
2. B	7. A	12. C	17. B
3. C	8. C	13. C	18. B
4. B	9. D	14. C	19. B
5. B	10. B	15. A	20. D

CHAPTER 11 FOOD WEBS MATTER

Chapter 11 Review

Page 68

1. C   2. C   3. A   4. D   5. D

CHAPTER 12 TRANSFER OF ENERGY

Chapter 12 Review

Page 72

1 . C   2. B   3. A   4. D   5. C

CHAPTER 13 ENVIROMENT AND ORGANISMS

Chapter 13 Review

Page 76

1. B   2. D   3. A   4. B   5. B

CHAPTER 14 ORGANISMS RELATIONSHIPS

Chapter 14 Review

Page 80

1. C   2. C   3. A   4. A   5. B

CHAPTER 15 EARTH'S BIOMES

Chapter 15 Review

Page 86

1. D   2. D   3. B   4. D   5. A

DOMAIN 2 REVIEW

Pages 87 – 90

1. B	6. C	11. B	16. A
2. B	7. B	12. B	17. D
3. A	8. B	13. D	18. C
4. D	9. B	14. C	19. C
5. C	10. A	15. C	20. D

CHAPTER 16 PHYSICAL CHANGE

Chapter 16 Review

Page 96

1. A   2. B   3. A   4. D   5. D

CHAPTER 17 NATURAL SELECTION

Chapter 17 Review

Page 102

1. A   2. D   3. C   4. B   5. D

CHAPTER 18 FOSSIL RECORD

Chapter 18 Review

Page106

1. A   2. B   3. D   4. C   5. A

DOMAIN 3 REVIEW

Pages 107 – 110

1. D	6. B	11. B	16. B
2. A	7. C	12. A	17. A
3. B	8. A	13. A	18. B
4. A	9. B	14. C	19. C
5. A	10. A	15. A	20. A

POST TEST 1

Pages 111 – 121

1. A	11. A	21. A	31. B	41. A	51. B
2. D	12. A	22. A	32. B	42. B	52. A
3. D	13. B	23. A	33. C	43. C	53. D
4. C	14. D	24. C	34. A	44. C	54. D
5. C	15. C	25. C	35. A	45. D	55. B
6. D	16. C	26. D	36. D	46. D	56. B
7. B	17. A	27. B	37. C	47. D	57. D
8. B	18. A	28. B	38. D	48. C	58. A
9. A	19. C	29. A	39. A	49. D	59. B
10. A	20. C	30. D	40. A	50. D	60. A

POST TEST 2

Pages 123 – 133

1. B	11. B	21. B	31. D	41. A	51. B
2. A	12. A	22. B	32. B	42. D	52. D
3. A	13. D	23. B	33. C	43. D	53. C
4. A	14. D	24. B	34. A	44. A	54. B

5. C	15. A	25. B	35. B	45. C	55. D
6. D	16. C	26. C	36. B	46. A	56. A
7. A	17. C	27. C	37. A	47. B	57. B
8. B	18. A	28. D	38. B	48. D	58. C
9. C	19. B	29. A	39. A	49. A	59. D
10. D	20. A	30. C	40. C	50. C	60. A

Product Order Form

Please fill this form out completely and fax it to 1-866-827-3240

American Book Company
Meeting Standards,
Exceeding Expectations

Purchase Order #: _____   Date: _____

Contact Person: _____

School Name (and District, if any): _____

_____

Billing Address: _____ Street Address: ☐ same as billing

_____   _____

Attn: _____   Attn: _____

_____   _____

_____   _____

Phone: _____ E-Mail: _____

Credit Card #: _____ Exp Date: _____

Authorized Signature: _____

Order Number	Product Title	Pricing* 5 books	Pricing* 30 books	Total Cost
GA5-M0806	Mastering the Georgia 5th Grade CRCT in Mathematics	$49.95 (1 set of 5 books)	$254.70 (1 set of 30 books)	
GA5-R1206	Mastering the Georgia 5th Grade CRCT in Reading	$49.95 (1 set of 5 books)	$254.70 (1 set of 30 books)	
GA6-M0305	Mastering the Georgia 6th Grade CRCT in Mathematics	$49.95 (1 set of 5 books)	$254.70 (1 set of 30 books)	
GA6-S1206	Mastering the Georgia 6th Grade CRCT in Science	$49.95 (1 set of 5 books)	$254.70 (1 set of 30 books)	
GA7-M0305	Mastering the Georgia 7th Grade CRCT in Mathematics	$49.95 (1 set of 5 books)	$254.70 (1 set of 30 books)	
GA7-S1206	Mastering the Georgia 7th Grade CRCT in Science	$49.95 (1 set of 5 books)	$254.70 (1 set of 30 books)	
GA8-M0305	Passing the Georgia 8th Grade CRCT in Mathematics	$49.95 (1 set of 5 books)	$254.70 (1 set of 30 books)	
GA8-L0505	Passing the Georgia 8th Grade CRCT in Language Arts	$49.95 (1 set of 5 books)	$254.70 (1 set of 30 books)	
GA8-R0505	Passing the Georgia 8th Grade CRCT in Reading	$49.95 (1 set of 5 books)	$254.70 (1 set of 30 books)	
GAMG-W0805	Preparing for the Georgia Middle Grades Writing Assessment	$49.95 (1 set of 5 books)	$254.70 (1 set of 30 books)	
GA-EOCL0806	Passing the Georgia 9th Grade Lit. and Comp. End of Course	$54.95 (1 set of 5 books)	$284.70 (1 set of 30 books)	
GA-EOCM0904	Passing the Georgia Algebra I End of Course	$54.95 (1 set of 5 books)	$284.70 (1 set of 30 books)	
GA-EOCB0805	Passing the Georgia Biology End of Course	$54.95 (1 set of 5 books)	$284.70 (1 set of 30 books)	
GA-EOCE0305	Passing the Georgia Economics End of Course	$54.95 (1 set of 5 books)	$284.70 (1 set of 30 books)	
GA-EOCG0505	Passing the Georgia Geometry End of Course	$54.95 (1 set of 5 books)	$284.70 (1 set of 30 books)	
GA-EOCP0106	Passing the Georgia Physical Science End of Course	$54.95 (1 set of 5 books)	$284.70 (1 set of 30 books)	
GA-EOCH0605	Passing the Georgia United States History End of Course	$54.95 (1 set of 5 books)	$284.70 (1 set of 30 books)	
GA-L1206	Passing the Georgia English Language Arts Graduation Test	$69.95 (1 set of 5 books)	$374.70 (1 set of 30 books)	
GA-M0705	Passing the Georgia Mathematics Graduation Test	$69.95 (1 set of 5 books)	$374.70 (1 set of 30 books)	
GA-S0806	Passing the Georgia Science Graduation Test	$69.95 (1 set of 5 books)	$374.70 (1 set of 30 books)	
GA-H0300N	Passing the Georgia Social Studies Graduation Test	$69.95 (1 set of 5 books)	$374.70 (1 set of 30 books)	
GA-W1000N	Passing the Georgia Writing Graduation Test	$69.95 (1 set of 5 books)	$374.70 (1 set of 30 books)	
Call for Order #	Passing the Georgia Graduation Test On-Line Testing**	$399.00 (1 year subscription)		

1-5-07

*Minimum order is 1 set of 5 books of the same subject.
**Each subscription is per subject. Only $299 for customers who have previously purchased a site license! If you qualify, please call us today to secure your lower price!

Subtotal _____

Shipping & Handling 10%
(- $100 per subscription for previous customers**) _____

Total _____

American Book Company ● PO Box 2638 ● Woodstock, GA 30188-1383
Toll Free: 1-888-264-5877 ● Fax: 1-866-827-3240 ● Web Site: www.americanbookcompany.com